# Choosing an Online Therapist

## A Step-by-Step Guide to Finding Professional Help on the Web

### Gary S. Stofle

White Hat Communications
Harrisburg, PA

# Choosing an Online Therapist
## A Step-by-Step Guide to
## Finding Professional Help on the Web

by Gary S. Stofle

Published by:

*White Hat Communications*

P.O. Box 5390 • Harrisburg, PA 17110-0390
717-238-3787 (voice)
717-238-2090 (fax)
http://www.socialworker.com

Copyright © 2001 Gary S. Stofle. All rights reserved. No part of this book may be reproduced or transmitted in any form or by any means, electronic or mechanical, including photocopying, recording, or by any information and retrieval system without written permission from the publisher, except for the inclusion of brief quotations in a review.

The information in this publication is not intended as a substitute for consultation with health care or mental health professionals. Each individual's health concerns should be evaluated by a qualified professional.

*Microsoft® Internet Explorer is a registered trademark of Microsoft Corporation. Microsoft® Internet Explorer browser screen shots reprinted by permission from Microsoft Corporation.*

Cover design by Alex Fidelibus
Photo of author by Bernie Larsen

**Library of Congress Cataloging-in-Publication Data**
Stofle, Gary S.
  Choosing an online therapist : a step-by-step guide to finding professional help on the web / by Gary S. Stofle.
     p. cm.
Includes index.
  ISBN 1-929109-05-9
  ISBN 1-929109-04-0 (e-book)
  1. Psychotherapists. 2. Psychotherapist and patient. 3. Psychotherapy—Computer network resources. 4. Internet. I. Title.
  RC480.5 .S689 2001
  616.89'14—dc21

                                        2001001124

# TABLE OF CONTENTS

*To Katie and Allie*
*Two of the best kids in the world—I love you.*

*To Alison*
*I couldn't have done it without your love and support.*
*You are my lover and my best friend.*

# Acknowledgments

First, I would like to thank my publisher, Linda Grobman. She had faith in me and in the ideas for this book from the start. She was kind and supportive throughout this process and yet held me to task. Thank you, Linda, for opening this door for me.

I would really like to thank all the clients and colleagues with whom I have worked online. They have been my teachers and have shown me the healing power of the Internet.

My mother has loved me through thick and thin. She has always believed in me. Thank you, Mom, for your emotional support over the years.

My in-laws, Al and Gloria Fidelibus, have been supportive of me and my family over the last twenty years in many ways. Quick to laugh and tease, Al is very engaging and is loved by all who know him. There is a poetic, sensitive side to him as well. He lives by the Golden Rule. Gloria is the quintessential Italian mother who cooks like an angel and whose love for people is bigger than the great outdoors. Thank you both for all your help and support.

Dr. Ron Olah, Susan Mankita, and Kate Anthony invested much time and energy in reviewing drafts of the manuscript. Each provided me with direct, precise, and helpful feedback, and this book is all the more readable and clear because of their comments. I'll forever be in their debt.

I would like to acknowledge three people who have been pivotal in my life over the last several years: Dr. John Wallace and Bernie and Roxy Larsen. Dr. Wallace is a model for the characteristics of an excellent therapist. He taught me many things during the time I worked with and for him, both by his words and his actions. He is quite accomplished in many areas and yet is never too busy or too accomplished to serve the needs of others. Thank you, John, for all you do and are and for the support you've given me over the last several years. Bernie and Roxy have been my spiritual guides over the last year and have been there, without fail, for me and for my family. Thank you both.

I would also like to thank Alex Fidelibus, my brother-in-law, for his work on the cover of this book. His art is both powerful and elegant. My other extended family members—Jim and Diane, Walt and Cathy, and Alex's wife Eri—have loved and supported me and my family all these years. Their excitement for me in this project has propelled me forward to completion.

My children, Katie and Allie, have put up with my preoccupation with this book and have shown me love and grace. Nothing is more wonderful to me than getting a big hug and kiss from one of my kids.

Last, and most assuredly not least, I would like to say thanks to my wife, Alison, for all her love and support. She has given me feedback about my ideas for this book and always helps me see the truth. She is a wise and beautiful woman. Thanks, Honey.

# Chapter 1
## The What and Why of Online Therapy

*What is online therapy?* you might be wondering. *Is it possible to get professional help online for personal or mental health problems?*

Online therapy is the provision of counseling or therapeutic services over the Internet (via e-mail, chat, audio, and video) by a licensed or credentialed mental health practitioner. This book focuses on e-mail and chat therapy, which are the main modalities online therapists are using as of this writing. Video interaction between therapist and client generally requires expensive equipment and a great amount of Internet bandwidth, so it has yet to become a major focus for private therapists and small companies. Even with technological advances and reduction in prices for video equipment, there will still be a number of people who will prefer text-based therapy over video. With e-mail and chat, all a therapist and a consumer need before they can work together online is a computer, a connection to the Internet, an Internet Service Provider (ISP), and the software the ISP provides.

Before we ask the question, "Why online therapy?" it is important to ask, "Why therapy?" After this question is answered satisfactorily, we can start to explore the issues and questions related to online therapy, such as: *Can online therapy work? Can online therapy work with the issues I am facing? What are the issues I need to be aware of in online therapy? How do I find a competent online therapist?*

So, why therapy? The answer is simple—people go to therapy because it works. Multiple studies show that psychotherapy is effective in helping people. The American Psychological Association has published an article online entitled "The Efficacy of Psychotherapy" (http://www.apa.org/practice/peff.html), which lists and discusses multiple studies. These studies clearly show that therapy is effective. *Consumer Reports* published a study on the effectiveness of psychotherapy in November 1995. Dr. Martin Seligman reviewed this study (http://mentalhelp.net/articles/seligm.htm) and described it as "the most extensive study of psychotherapy effectiveness on record." He discussed a number of "clear-cut results" of the study, the first one being: "Treatment by a mental health professional usually worked. Most respondents got a lot better."

Therapy helps us change our lives. It teaches us skills and helps us see ourselves in a more realistic light. Therapy helps us get rid of misconceptions about ourselves and the world and also helps us function better both in the world and more specifically in relationships. Therapy can help fill that gaping hole inside that some of us feel. It can teach us how to live effectively with illness, whether that illness is mental or physical. Therapy can help us find relief from emotional pain. Therapy can help us deal with the stress of living in a very chaotic and complicated world. In general, therapy can help us be better partners, parents, lovers, and people. It can help us find the peace and happiness we deserve.

Therapy comes in many forms today: Cognitive Behavioral Therapy, Rational Emotive Behavioral Therapy, Narrative Therapy, Transactional Analysis, Person Centered Therapy, and Humanistic Therapy, just to name a few. Some types of therapy will be briefly discussed in Appendix C for the interested reader.

If face-to-face (F2F) therapy works well, why consider online therapy? Well, the truth is, many people would rather participate in therapy face-to-face as opposed to online. I've had e-mail exchanges with people who needed information concerning what to do about a problem, and when I suggest they seek therapy, they often say, "Can you refer me to a therapist in my area?" When I tell them about the possibility of online therapy, they don't want to hear about it. "What? I need to see the therapist I'm talking to." Even though many people (and therapists) prefer face-to-face therapy, there are more and more people and therapists who are interested in online therapy. Here are some reasons why:

1. *Geography.* Some people are isolated geographically, and it can be quite a problem because of physical distance to get to a clinic or a private therapist's office. Even if access to a good therapist locally is not a problem for you, you are not bound by the limits of geography when you are online. You can access a therapist in another state or on another continent! You can find a treatment expert who specializes in the issues you face and access that person wherever he or she may be. It's wild to think you can live in Des Moines and can be in treatment with a therapist in Hong Kong!

2. *Disability.* Certain disabilities limit a person's ability to travel even short distances. This is a non-issue in online therapy, because you don't have to leave your home. Equipment can be purchased that enables people with a wide variety of disabilities to effectively use the computer and be able to benefit from online therapy.

3. *Shame/guilt.* Some people don't seek therapy because they feel ashamed or guilty. Many have been raised to believe people are "crazy" if they need to see a counselor. Fortunately, this stigma has been reduced in recent years, in part, perhaps, as a result of education that is available on the Internet. Recent articles tell us that it is easier to "open up" online than it is in face-to-face therapy. People who have accessed online therapy tend to be more open more quickly, thus moving the therapeutic process along.

4. *Community status.* Some seek online therapy because their status in the community could be affected by their seeking any type of counseling. Although all ethical therapists and agencies abide by the laws of confidentiality, there is nothing that prevents a neighbor from seeing my car in the Mental Health Center parking lot every Tuesday night at 7 p.m. People in sensitive positions (mayor, police chief, city councilperson, and the like) deserve the right to access therapy as well as the rest of us. This issue applies in any instance in which the public's perception of a person has a large effect (as in the perception of a corporation's CEO and the effect that has on the corporation's stocks, for example).

5. *Social phobia/panic attacks.* People who suffer from ago-raphobia or panic attacks often have great difficulty leaving their homes. Online therapy is the logical choice for these folks. I've talked to colleagues who report success in helping people online with these issues.

*Does online therapy work?* Clearly, not enough studies have been done to say scientifically that online therapy works. Many authors discuss anecdotal evidence of how well online therapy works. Also, there are a number of research projects going on to examine this issue. The International Society of Mental Health Online (http://www.ismho.org/) created a Clinical Case Study Group to discuss "psychotherapy cases and professional clinical encounters that involve the Internet" in the fall of 1999. Organized and facilitated by John Suler and Michael Fenichel, this group is one of the first to conduct a systematic investigation of online therapy. More information about this group can be found at http://www.rider.edu/users/suler/psycyber/casegrp.html. Sixteen therapists discussed psychotherapeutic interventions that they conducted either totally or partially online. The cases presented consistently demonstrated the fact that therapeutic interventions conducted by ethical therapists can be provided online and the clients respond in a positive manner.

There are obvious concerns regarding online therapy:

1. *Non-verbal cues.* Your therapist can't physically see you and so will miss the "non-verbal" cues that help in communication between two people.

2. *Accessibility.* A great distance may separate you from the therapist, and that prevents the therapist from intervening in a crisis the way he or she would if you were sitting in the same room.

3. *Questions of effectiveness.* As discussed above, not enough research has been conducted to prove the effectiveness of online therapy. Some mental health clinicians are very vocal in their opposition to online therapy for this reason. They say it is unethical to practice where no scientific evidence exists. (Others think it is unethical *not* to practice where there is a need.)

4. *Potential for fraud.* Identity can be a problem. Is the therapist who he says he is? And of concern for the therapist—are you who you say you are?

5. *Confidentiality.* Will the information you reveal be revealed to people you didn't intend to tell, either intentionally or inadvertently?

Online therapists and online therapy companies are working on these and other concerns.

*Can online therapy help you with the issues you face?* The answer is the same for any type of therapy—it depends upon what your issues are. The concept of Level of Care is discussed in Chapter 2, *Can You Benefit From Online Therapy?* This chapter looks at the characteristics of a person who would most benefit from an online therapy level of care. The maxim is: the more intense the problem(s), the more intense the intervention needs to be. There are some problems that obviously should not be treated online and these are discussed in this chapter. Online therapy is a level of care that is an entirely appropriate modality of treatment for certain issues and problems. The Level of Care Table on page 29 shows what issues and problems should be treated online and which problems/issues need to be treated in face-to-face therapy.

*What qualities or characteristics do you need to look for in a good online therapist?* Chapter 3, *Characteristics of a Good Online Therapist,* looks at these qualities. Research has shown that certain characteristics in a therapist tend to be associated with good outcomes in treatment, no matter what type of therapy the therapist practices. These characteristics are discussed in this chapter. It is important to note that these qualities are particularly essential to online therapy. The "relationship" is the thing in online therapy. You can't develop a relationship with an online therapist who doesn't type, however. So, in addition to the essential qualities generally associated with successful treatment, the therapist needs other skills, both technical and nontechnical, which are specific to online therapy. This chapter looks at those issues, as well. Even the most famous and effective therapists would not be successful conducting therapy online if they lacked these extra qualities.

So, you've concluded that online therapy is right for you and you know what to look for in an online therapist. *What's next?* Chapter 4, *Nuts and Bolts—Practical Issues in Online Therapy,* examines key issues relevant to online therapy. These issues include: types of online therapy, finding an online therapist, confidentiality, fees, licensing, different types of therapists, scheduling, and charting.

*What do you need to know to be more comfortable about the first session?* Chapter 5, *The First Session,* explores common initial feelings related to this important time. To be prepared for the first session, you need to think about why you are seeking treatment and what you want out of it. What are your goals for treatment—what needs to change in your life, and what do you want your life to look like when you are finished with therapy? These issues and treatment planning are covered in this chapter.

The next part of this process, after the initial sessions, is your participation in therapy. That is the work. That is where you can look at yourself, look at the things that don't work so well in your life and then begin to make the changes you need to make. This part is not easy, and if it is, you probably aren't doing therapy with your therapist. This part in the process is not addressed in this book, because it is so idiosyncratic to your experience that it would be beyond the scope of this book to try to cover all the issues concerned with the treatment itself. For some thoughts about the work in therapy, you can go to the following Web sites:

http://www.aboutpsychotherapy.com/
http://suite101.com/welcome.cfm/psychotherapy_self_help

Chapter 6, *Terminating Therapy,* looks at how to end therapy in either a planned or unplanned manner. Your right to terminate treatment is looked at, as well as some signs that the treatment is completed. Also, and importantly, this chapter explores what to do if there are significant problems in your relationship with your therapist.

Appendix A, *Getting Online and Basic Communications Skills,* is written for the reader who wants to access online therapy, but has no online experience at all and isn't "connected." This appendix can be useful if you are just looking for your first computer or if you want to upgrade your current computer and need some suggestions. Topics in this appendix include buying hardware and software, selecting an Internet Service Provider, and Netiquette. This chapter also includes a listing of symbols and abbreviations commonly used online.

Appendix B contains two sets of standards for online therapy: the National Board of Certified Counselors' "Standards for the Ethical Practice of WebCounseling" and the International Society of Mental Health Online's "ISMHO/PSI Suggested Principles for the Online Provision of Mental Health Services."

Appendix C is a sampling of some of the major schools of therapy and a brief explanation of each. This listing is not meant to be exhaustive. It will help you have a better understanding of the types of therapy, so you can understand your therapist's orientation, beliefs, and ideas about therapy.

Appendix D is a database of 12 online therapists and 8 e-therapy company sites. These are not ranked in any way, and no endorsement of any particular site or therapist is made by either the author or the publisher. They are listed as examples of the kinds of sites you might find through your own search. These sites were found by a simple Internet search. Sites that were a part of the search results that did not include identifying information about the therapist were not included in this database.

So, there you have it. My hope is that through reading this book, the question for you will change from "Why online therapy?" to "Why *not* online therapy?"

*eTherapy.com (http://www.etherapy.com) is an online therapy company where you can search for a licensed therapist in your own state. Copyright 2000 eTherapy.com, Inc. Reprinted with permission.*

# Chapter 2
## Can You Benefit From Online Therapy?

Online therapy can be thought of as falling into certain "levels of care" and is an entirely appropriate way for professionals to provide help for certain issues and problems. Level of care simply means there are varying levels of intensity of the treatment, which needs to match up to the intensity of the problem. Online therapy is on the lower intensity side of the level of care continuum, and so is best used for issues/problems that are on the lower intensity side, as well. Below is a diagram illustrating the concept of level of care.

Most Intensive                                    Least Intensive

❶              ❷              ❸              ❹              ❺

❶ *Inpatient Psychiatric Hospitalization.* This is the most intensive level of care for mental health concerns and is generally reserved for people who are a clear and present danger to themselves or to others. One of the most intense interventions at this level is called "Constant Observation," which means that someone is with the client twenty-four hours per day, watching and monitoring her to make sure she doesn't hurt herself or someone else. The practice of deeming a person "crazy" and then "locking them up and throwing away the key" is simply not done anymore. (See the section on suicide on pages 21-22.) The typical length of stay in psychiatric hospitals has drastically decreased over the last ten years. The whole point of inpatient psychiatric hospitalization is to get the patient stabilized so he or she can be safely discharged from the hospital. Online therapy is **not appropriate** for people with issues and problems that need treatment at this level of care.

❷ *Partial Hospitalization.* This level of care is similar to being in the hospital. Clients have many of the same services, but they go home at night. Services typically are provided six days per week, often from 9 a.m. to 4 p.m. Many supportive and group/individual interventions are offered at this level of care. In much the same way as inpatient hospitalization, a person only stays in this level of care as long as the symptoms indicate a need for this intense service. The work and focus of treatment is to stabilize the person to a higher level of functioning. As a person's functioning increases, he or she needs less intensive services. Online therapy is **not appropriate** for people with issues and problems that need treatment at this level of care.

❸ *Day Hospital.* This level is less intense than partial hospitalization, but generally requires daily (weekday) participation in group and individual sessions for at least three hours per day (and often more). Many people who are in need of day hospital treatment have chronic psychiatric problems that need the support of daily contact and monitoring. Online therapy is **generally not appropriate** for this level of care. I can forsee therapists who work in day hospitals making the case for online therapy with their clients if certain conditions are met: 1) online therapy is done as an adjunct to face-to-face treatment, 2) the person receiving the service is taking medication as directed, 3) the therapist conducting the face-to-face treatment is also the online therapist, and, most importantly, 4) the client is amenable to online therapy.

❹ *Intensive Outpatient.* This level of care involves about nine hours of therapy per week—usually three evenings, three hours per evening. Many people with alcohol or substance abuse problems obtain treatment at this level of care. Again, this is generally done on a short-term basis with very specific goals that need to be accomplished in order to improve the person's functioning. With successful completion of therapy at this level, the client moves to less intense treatment. Online therapy **may be appropriate** for people with issues and problems requiring services at this level of intensity.

❺ *Outpatient.* This is the least intense level of treatment, for people with issues or problems that would benefit from mental health interventions. The number of contacts can range from several times per week to one time per month. All personal growth counseling falls into this category. People whose issues or problems require this level of intervention **can be ideal** candidates for online therapy.

Therapists who are vocal in their belief that therapy can't ethically occur online seem to disregard the issue of level of care as noted above. The statement "online therapy is not ethical" does not take into account that every level and type of treatment is appropriate in certain situations and is not appropriate in others. Someone who needs constant observation should not be in a type of treatment in which observation is impossible. Conversely, someone who is in need of personal growth counseling doesn't need a partial hospital or an inpatient hospital treatment level of care.

The issue of level of care should be of concern to both the therapist and the person receiving the service throughout the therapy process. A person's needs can change at any time, and both the therapist and the consumer need to be able to respond by changing the type of treatment, based upon the issues presented. If a therapist is working with someone who becomes acutely suicidal, then action needs to be taken immediately. For online therapy to work properly, this action needs to be discussed and agreed upon in advance, and in the case of suicidality, must involve the client's agreement to get an immediate face-to-face evaluation, generally in an emergency room.

Suicidality and other issues that cannot be treated online are discussed in the next section. These issues are ones that generally require treatment in the first three levels of care, as noted above.

## Level of Care and Requirements of Treatment as a Barrier to Treatment

Following the maxim, "the most intensive level of problems needs the most intensive level of treatment," it is easy for a knowledgeable clinician to assess a person and make a clear recommendation for a level of care. There are problems with the concept of level of care treatment, however:

1. Treatment at the needed level of care might be unavailable, unavailable now, or not affordable by the person seeking treatment.

2. The person seeking treatment may want a different (usually less intensive) level of care.

3. Insurance may not cover the cost of the appropriate level of care.

At this point, both the therapist and the person seeking treatment need to decide if they want to follow through with treatment at a level of care different from the most appropriate level. The choice is often between treatment at the wrong level of care and no treatment.

This same issue occurs when conventional treatment wisdom is confronted. An example is this: Alcoholism counselors believe a person must stop drinking to benefit from outpatient alcoholism counseling. However, many clients who are referred to treatment don't want to stop drinking. The choice these potential clients face is to either stop drinking or receive no treatment.

This level of care discrepancy will be faced over and over again by online therapists. You, as a potential consumer of online therapy, may have issues and problems that are in fact better treated in face-to-face therapy. You may have made your mind up, however, that you will not seek face-to-face therapy. Understand that this is an issue that both you and your therapist will have to consider and negotiate. Some therapists are willing to resist the conventional wisdom, because they believe that some treatment (even at the wrong level) is better than no treatment at all. Other therapists will not treat you in online therapy if they think you would be better served in face-to-face therapy.

# Issues/Problems <u>Not</u> Appropriately Treated Online

## Suicidality

***This may be one of the most important sections in this book. Please read it carefully.*** The issue of suicide and the potential loss of a person's life is probably the main reason why some therapists won't work online. When the therapist has a client in her office, and the client is acutely suicidal (he reveals a plan to kill himself and has both the means and the intent to follow through with that plan), the therapist must act immediately to insure that person's safety. If the client doesn't want to do what is necessary in order to be safe, the therapist has to take control. I know from experience that this scenario is one of the most intense interventions in the life of a therapist. The therapist can't make a mistake. Acute suicidality requires a face-to-face intervention—nothing less will do. The principle used here on the part of the therapist is to "err on the side of caution." Online therapy is **not appropriate** for a person who is acutely suicidal. **If you are reading this, and you are having thoughts of killing yourself, call 911 or the National Hopeline Network's 1-800-SUICIDE hotline. This number will direct you to your local suicide hotline.**

It is important for you, the reader of this book, to understand how modern mental health treatment works. If you grew up with a *One Flew Over the Cuckoo's Nest* idea of mental health treatment, you have the mistaken belief that if "they" think you are "crazy," you could be stuck in a mental institution indefinitely. Well, that just is not the case anymore. If you have ever said to yourself, "If someone only knew what I really thought, I'd be locked up," understand that today, that is not likely to happen. People are only hospitalized if they are an immediate danger to themselves or others, and they remain hospitalized only as long as it takes to help them regain stability.

I am taking a long time to say that if you are suicidal at any time, it is important to let someone know, so you can get the care you need. If you do need hospitalization, take comfort in knowing it will only be until your condition has stabilized and you are safe. A person who has used online therapy appropriately, then because of acute suicidal ideation needs hospitalization, can later be seen online again once he or she is stabilized.

There are different types of suicidality. I have been talking about being acutely suicidal, but there is also "suicidal ideation" without a plan and passive suicidal ideation (having suicidal thoughts). Having suicidal ideation without a plan means that you have a desire to kill yourself, but you haven't thought about a way or a means to actually do it. There are some people who have chronic feelings of suicide, but have not attempted suicide and may never do so. These folks need an intense level of treatment to insure their safety, until they get to the point that this ideation either stops or they can successfully manage it. Passive suicidal ideation is shown by a person who doesn't actively think of killing himself, but who might say something like, "Well, if I don't wake up in the morning, that's okay with me." A person with passive suicidal ideation may be treated with online therapy, particularly if he or she is willing to contract with the therapist to follow certain steps if the suicidality becomes acute.

If you have experienced *any* of these types of suicidality, you will need to be assessed by a professional to determine the most appropriate course of treatment for you.

### Disordered Thinking

People who have disordered thinking are not appropriate candidates for online therapy. A person with disordered thinking might be diagnosed with schizophrenia or schizoaffective disorder. Other types of mental illnesses can cause the same types of problems. People who have disordered thinking have difficulty separating out what is real and what is not real. They can have unusual thoughts, such as thinking that someone on the radio or TV is talking directly to them or someone is inserting thoughts in their heads. Sometimes a person may think he is someone he is not and does not believe real information about himself. A person who is currently struggling with this type of illness will most often need one of the first three types of treatment noted above: 1) inpatient psychiatric hospitalization, 2) partial hospitalization, or 3) day hospital. Once stabilized on medication, he or she can be treated at an outpatient level of care.

## Borderline Personality Disorder

People who have been diagnosed with borderline personality disorder may not be appropriate candidates for online therapy. A person with this diagnosis needs to have regular face-to-face contact with a therapist over time in order to begin to learn the skills needed to deal with the many issues and problems she faces. For more information about borderline personality disorder, go to http://www.bpdcentral.com/links/links.htm. Online therapy might be used at some point, however, as an adjunct to face-to-face treatment. Clear boundaries would need to be set prior to any online treatment process. A large part of therapists' resistance to working online with people who are diagnosed with borderline personality disorder is the great difficulty these clients have with interpersonal relationships. One of the symptoms of this disorder is intense, unstable interpersonal relationships.

Online therapy (as well as face-to-face) depends upon the formation of a therapeutic relationship. Some people have a great deal of difficulty establishing and forming relationships with others. I am not talking about having problems or difficulties in relationships—we all have those, and general relationship issues can be dealt with in online interventions. However, there are some people whose relationships are constantly intense and unstable. These folks lack needed skills in managing relationships. These skills are best learned in face-to-face therapy.

How would you know if this applies to you? You need to ask yourself several questions:

1.  Do you alternate between really liking someone and then really disliking that same person, with most of your relationships?

2.  Do you expect others to be perfect and when they are not, you want to end the relationship with them?

3.  Are you easily hurt in relationships, even when that was not the intention of the other person? Do you hold on to that hurt even when it is apparent that doing so is not in your best interest?

4. Have you ever intentionally injured yourself, such as cutting your arms?

If you answered yes to these questions, it will be best for you to seek face-to-face therapy, at least initially.

## Medical Issues

Sometimes mental health treatment also has a medical component. What comes to mind to illustrate this point is anorexia nervosa. The person who suffers from anorexia will often have physical complications. It is my opinion that any mental health issue with a physical component should be treated face-to-face rather than online, at least initially.

There may be eating disorder specialists who could argue that online therapy can be accomplished, provided the person who seeks treatment allows coordination of treatment services between the face-to-face physician and the online therapist.

Additionally, anyone who seeks mental health services should have a complete physical examination prior to starting any mental health treatment. There are diseases that cause symptoms that can be mistaken for depression, and all the psychotherapy in the world is not going to resolve the depression until the medical problems are addressed. Hypothyroidism is a disease that causes depression in its sufferers, and it is simply and effectively treated by daily medication, which resolves the depression in a matter of weeks. **Again, obtain a physical examination before starting any type of psychotherapy, either online or face-to-face.**

# Issues/Problems That <u>Can</u> Be Treated Online

If you do not suffer from any of the above problems, you may still be a candidate for online therapy. Several issues or problems that *can* be treated online are discussed in this section. This is not meant to be an exhaustive list, and as therapists get more experience and comfort online, the list will surely grow. The issues noted below are treatable at the outpatient level of care.

## Personal Growth and Fulfillment

*John has all the trappings of a successful life and career, and yet feels unfulfilled in his relationship with his wife. He loves his wife greatly, but has difficulty opening up to her (despite wanting to open up). John could benefit from online therapy to help him learn the skills he needs to learn to be able to communicate with his wife.*

*Sylvia is functional in the world, but hates her life. She goes through the motions every day, and a person who meets her would say she has a good life. However, she is miserable most days and although she has never thought of doing something to end her life, she has gone to bed on many occasions hoping she just wouldn't wake up the next day. Sylvia could benefit from online therapy.*

Issues of personal growth and fulfillment can and are being treated online. People in this group are those who don't have psychiatric diagnoses, but who deserve and would benefit from counseling and therapy to help them live more effectively. Sometimes people in this group have "made it" in the world and yet feel unfulfilled. Many times people in this group seek therapy because they lack intimacy in their relationships and have difficulty dealing with feelings. All of these types of issues can be dealt with online.

## Adult Children of Alcoholics

*Jerry's mother was an alcoholic. He learned growing up that it was more important to focus on others than himself. As a consequence, he never learned how to take care of his basic feeling needs. Jerry would benefit from online therapy to learn basic feelings awareness skills.*

*Mary has been involved in abusive relationships all her life after leaving her home, where both parents were alcoholic. She can't understand how she keeps getting involved with men who are not good for her. Mary would benefit from online therapy to help her understand how growing up in an alcoholic home continues to affect the choices she makes and then free her to make other, more self caring choices.*

I have worked with several Adult Children of Alcoholics (ACOAs) online with success. The issues that many ACOAs face—problems dealing with feelings, self esteem issues, lack of self care skills, problems with trust and intimacy, unawareness of one's own needs, and so on—can be effectively dealt with online. Challenging mistaken beliefs about oneself and the world can easily be done online. Other techniques that make sense to use online—journaling, other cognitive behavioral therapy work, feelings diary, homework assignments, narrative therapy—all are techniques and types of therapy used in working with ACOAs.

The issues ACOAs face can be assessed in one session. In the same session, information can be given to the person about the specific changes that need to be made in order for that person to find peace and happiness. However, from my experience, it takes months or even years of work for a person to make these changes. The ACOA often needs a therapist who can "be there" to provide guidance, feedback, and support over this time. The issues that an ACOA often faces develop over years and are quite difficult to undo.

### Agoraphobia/Anxiety Disorders/Social Phobia

*Martha is afraid to travel by car and is quite fearful of crossing bridges. Whenever traveling and particularly when crossing over a bridge, she feels as if she is going to die. Unfortunately, she lives in a city with many bridges and so has difficulty accessing a therapist face-to-face. Martha could easily access therapy online from the comfort of her own home.*

Other problems that can be treated online are disorders that prevent a person from participating in the world. When a person is afraid to be around people, what better way to get treatment than online? It is much easier to open up to another looking at a computer screen than it is to open up in front of a live person, particularly when working from the safety and comfort of one's own home. With the support of a knowledgeable and caring therapist, the person who suffers from these disorders can establish a strong and therapeutic relationship with the online therapist. As the strength of this connection grows, the client can use the relationship as a jumping off point for further growth.

## Body Image Issues/Problems

*Mindy is morbidly obese and has been overweight her entire life. She was teased mercilessly growing up and consequently is uncomfortable in most social situations. Her self-consciousness has prevented her from seeking face-to-face therapy, although she believes it could help her deal with her many issues. Online therapy is more readily accessible to Mindy, because her weight is not a barrier to the treatment process.*

Many people have significant concerns related to their physical appearance. Some of us have been horrendously teased as children and adults because of our physical appearance, which causes pain of such a great extent that it's almost unspeakable.

One of the most beautiful aspects of text-based online therapy is it doesn't matter what you look like at all—no one knows online. You could weigh 350 pounds or 80 pounds; you could be the most attractive person in the world or the least; you could be the most athletic person or multiply disabled—it simply doesn't matter, as long as you can input your thoughts, ideas, and feelings into the computer. It doesn't even matter if you type or use your voice to input text—the method is transparent to the reader. Online therapy gives you a chance to work directly on matters of the heart, bypassing matters of the flesh.

Do body image issues and problems need to be addressed? Absolutely. But they can be addressed as a part of a larger healing process that can happen online over time. As the person with these issues works through uncomfortable feelings about how he or she looks and is anchored in the strength and understanding of the therapist, he or she can then move outward from the therapeutic relationship toward other relationships to try out new behaviors, and to find and develop relationships with other people who are understanding and supportive of the specific situation. This transformation is quite possible online.

## Shame/Guilt Issues

*Robert is a 65-year-old man who grew up thinking, "If you seek counseling, you must be crazy." He is on the verge of retiring, however, and is very concerned about the many changes that his retirement will bring. He simply needs some support during this upcoming time of transition, but also doesn't want to seek any counseling locally, because of his position on the school board. Brief e-mail therapy could provide him with what he needs to get through this difficult time in his life.*

In the past, people have avoided therapy because of feelings of shame and guilt. It sometimes takes quite an act of courage to go from home to a mental health clinic and talk about how your life is not working out. It can be so uncomfortable *(What if one of my neighbors sees me?)* that some never seek the treatment they need and deserve. That is the true shame. You might be struggling with an issue that can easily be helped through talking to a therapist, but you will never know it if you don't try it. How many of us are sitting at home, suffering silently, day after day?

In an ideal world, going to psychotherapy would feel no more "shameful" than going to the dentist or your family doctor. Society would actually praise you for getting the professional services you need. But for now, we still have a long way to go to erase the stigma that has been associated with mental health services. With the advent of online therapy, feelings of shame and guilt are less likely to be barriers for a person seeking treatment services.

## Level of Care Table[1]

| | Suicidality/ Homicidality | Relationships with others | Participation in the world | Reality Testing | Feelings Issues |
|---|---|---|---|---|---|
| Level 5 Outpatient *Online Therapy | No suicidal thoughts or occasional passive suicidal ideation. No homicidal thoughts. | Problems in relationships. Difficulty with openness and intimacy. Blames others. | Participates actively in the world, but doesn't reveal inner life to any others; lacks intimacy. | Has erroneous beliefs about self. Doesn't see self as worthwhile; self esteem problems. | Lacks feelings awareness skills, which causes ongoing uncomfortable feelings. |
| Level 4 Intensive Outpatient *Online Therapy Possible | Passive suicidal ideation. Angry feelings toward others with no plan to act them out, no intent. | Problems in relationships cause great distress. | Some difficulty with active participation in the world; lacks skills in dealing with people. | Mistaken beliefs about the world impair ability to be successful (temporarily) | Feelings affect life in a manner that reaches crisis proportions. |
| Level 3 Day Treatment | Suicidal thoughts but no plans or intent. Responds to support. Difficulty managing angry feelings toward others but responds to direction. | Intense, unstable interpersonal relationships | Participation in the world is limited to family and few friends or inappropriate support system. | Chronic problems with disordered thinking are managed by medication and support through day treatment. | Feelings are managed through support and training. |
| Level 2 Partial Hospital | Suicidal with a plan but can contract for safety. Angry feelings require monitoring by others to manage them. | Intense, unstable interpersonal relationships. | Therapist works to break isolation with daily therapeutic contact. | Needs support in order to function at a basic level outside of the hospital. | Feelings interfere with multiple aspects of life —functioning not possible without daily support. |
| Level 1 Inpatient Hospital | Acutely suicidal or acutely homicidal | Not applicable | Isolated from the world. [2] | Disordered thinking impairs basic functioning. | Feelings impair ability to function at a basic level. |

[1]The statements in each block are representative of issues for that level of care. These statements are made to give the reader an idea of the issues to be dealt with at that level of care. All Level 1 issues need at minimum a psychiatric evaluation to determine the appropriate level of care.
[2]May not need inpatient treatment.

# Chapter 3
## Characteristics of a Good Online Therapist

Research has shown that certain qualities are associated with positive outcomes in therapy. These are the qualities that you want in any therapist, including those who work online. Several of these characteristics are discussed here. Additionally, there are unique qualities that are essential for the online therapy experience—these are not needed for face-to-face therapy.

## Basic Qualifications of a Therapist (Face-to-Face or Online)

### Empathy

Multiple studies show empathy is the most important quality in a therapist. Dr. William Miller studied different interventions with groups of clients and found that one therapist's clients were getting better no matter what intervention she used. Empathy was the key to her success. Many other studies show the same thing. Carl Rogers, a noted psychologist who developed Person Centered Therapy, referred extensively to empathy in his many writings. He wrote, "The ideal therapist is, first of all, empathic," and, "To my mind, empathy is in itself a healing agent...."

Empathy is different from sympathy. Empathy is the ability of your therapist to perceive and understand the world from your point of view in a non-judgmental manner. He or she can see the world from your frame of reference. Empathy goes farther than simply understanding the words you say—it is understanding the meaning behind your words. When you share a problem or issue with an empathetic therapist, the therapist responds to you in such a way that you leave the interaction feeling understood and having learned more about yourself. Most of us are hungry for this feeling, because we seldom get it in our day-to-day lives. When we run across people who are empathetic, we tend to call them up when we are troubled or have problems. When I am empathetic with you, I can put myself in your place and see the world from your eyes, and yet still keep myself separate from you.

Sympathy is the process of feeling with another person, in order to help and support him or her. It is taking on another's feelings and feeling them with the other person. Sympathy is a very needed part of our lives and comes to us through supportive relationships. We need others to express sympathy to us when we lose a loved one and in other situations, as well. Sympathy has limited uses in therapy, however. If the therapist gets too caught up in how you are feeling and takes on your feelings, he or she becomes less able to guide, direct, teach, and intervene with you.

Here are examples of a sympathy response and an empathy response:

> *You: I was talking to Jane the other day about something I thought was pretty important—an insight I had about my relationship with my mom—and when I was finished, she simply said "oh" and then started talking about her garden.*

> *Your friend (sympathetic): That wasn't very nice what she did! How could she? She shouldn't have done that to you. I'm getting angry just thinking about that.*

> *Your therapist (empathetic): You must have felt pretty hurt and angry by her lack of response. I know what you were saying was very important to you. You felt unimportant, huh?*

Empathy is directly related to the next characteristic—caring/compassion.

### Caring/Compassion

Caring and compassion are two essential qualities of a good therapist. Caring seems to be a quality that a person either has or doesn't have—I don't think people can learn how to be caring. (They *may* be able to learn how to *behave* in a caring manner, however.) When a person is caring, he shows concern and attentiveness toward another person. He values the other person and has what psychotherapist Carl Rogers called "unconditional positive regard." If you have ever been the recipient of unconditional positive regard, you understand how important this is in the process of therapy. Most of us have had the experience of *conditional* positive regard, in which we gain affection and respect only if we do certain things, or do things in a certain way (get the "A," get the promotion, win the race). The affection and respect are conditional, based upon our performance. What we look for in a therapist is a person who has regard for us despite our flaws, because our flaws are the focus in therapy. The therapist has a positive sense about us without conditions. I've had clients who were very afraid of telling me about something that they had done that was wrong. They expect to hear, "How could you!?" when they reveal this thing about which they feel ashamed. Instead, they get an, "Okay, let's process this," with an attitude of acceptance.

Compassion is closely related to caring. Compassion is meant here to be a general "liking" of people and a desire to help people in need. Therapy cannot simply be a "job" for the therapist. Therapy doesn't work well that way. Therapists need to have some passion for this type of work or they can't do it well. (I've always said therapy is hard to do well, but easy to do poorly.) Compassion allows the therapist to put the needs of the client first. This means the therapist can tolerate some discomfort on his or her part in order to help you.

However, caring and compassion are impotent without knowledge.

## Knowledge

While empathy and caring/compassion set the stage for you to be able to do the work of therapy with the therapist, the therapist's knowledge allows the work to be done. The therapist has to have an understanding of the issues you face and must have an idea of how to help you move from where you are to where you want to be.

Knowledge allows the therapist to be competent. All ethical codes require competence on the part of the therapist. This competence means that the therapist knows "how things work." They also know how to "fill in the blanks." Filling in the blanks means that you can talk about an issue or problem, and the therapist probably has dealt with a similar issue somewhere in his or her treatment experience with others. When you work with an experienced therapist, it can be a bit spooky in the sense that you might think he can read your mind. He can't—he just knows how things work. This ability to fill in the blanks is essential for online therapy, because of the limited information available to the therapist when using typed text as opposed to being face to face with you. As discussed earlier, no non-verbal cues are available to the therapist using e-mail or chat.

There are many different schools of thought, or theories, of therapy. Each school has its beliefs about human growth and development and what needs to happen for an individual to be fully functioning. It is beyond the scope of this book to compare, contrast, and discuss the merits of the various types of therapy. Actually, many therapists today are "eclectic" in their approach to therapy, meaning they use whatever theory and interventions are needed to help a particular person at a particular time. If you are depressed, the therapist may use Cognitive Behavioral Therapy for the most part, but also some techniques from Rational Emotive Therapy and Gestalt in the work with you. For those interested, Appendix C contains a listing and brief explanation of many of the major schools of therapy. The main questions you have to ask yourself (as a consumer of online therapy services) are: *Does this therapist seem to know what he or she is talking about? Does this therapist seem grounded in his or her belief system about therapy and helping people?*

### Worthy of Trust (Trustworthy)

It is not wise to simply trust your therapist from the first meeting. Trust is something that develops over time, as you see that the therapist follows through with what she says she is going to do. The therapist needs to be consistent in his or her responses to you, and to only promise things he or she can deliver.

## Credentialed/Licensed

Stated simply, the therapist you choose should have the proper education and credentials. The type of degree, credential, or license will vary depending upon the profession of the therapist (such as social worker, psychologist, counselor, or psychiatrist) and upon the state in which the therapist lives. Common credentials are Licensed Independent Social Worker (LISW), Licensed Clinical Social Worker (LCSW), Licensed Professional Counselor (LPC), Certified Alcoholism Counselor (CAC), licensed psychologist, and medical doctor (MD). (The exact titles vary from state to state.) States credential therapists to prevent charlatans from practicing and harming people. A breakdown of professions and credentials is contained in the grid on the next page.

Therapists must go through testing and have a combination of education and experience in order to be credentialed. The therapists who go through this process are deemed by the state to be skillful enough to practice psychotherapy independently.

If the therapist you choose to work with online is credentialed, you have avenues for redress if there are problems in the therapy. You can always contact the board or agency that credentialed your therapist and complain. The credentialing agencies follow up on complaints and will go as far as taking away a therapist's license to practice, if the offense is serious enough.

Many current online therapists inform you of their credentials through a direct link to the licensing/credentialing board's home page. Some online therapy companies use a service called HSP Verified, Inc. to verify the credentials of their therapists. You can find information about HSP Verified at http:// www.hspverified.com/.

If you choose an online therapist who posts his or her credentials on a Web site without links or verification, you can call the therapist's state board and verify this information yourself. State boards will let you know whether or not what the therapist is claiming is in fact true. Additionally, the phone number and/or Web site of the board is also important for you to have if your therapist acts unethically. Dr. John Grohol has included

| Title | Degree | Licensure/ Credential | Comments |
|---|---|---|---|
| Psychologist | Ph.D. or Psy.D. | Licensed Psychologist | Cannot prescribe medicine. Psychologists who practice psychotherapy usually have degrees in *clinical* psychology. |
| Psychiatrist | M.D. or D.O. | Medical Doctor with a specialty in psychiatry and/or board certification | Can be a therapist. |
| Social worker | MSW, MSSW | LISW, LCSW, CSW, RCSW, LSW, depending upon the state | Cannot prescribe medicine. Many therapists are clinical social workers. |
| Professional counselors | M.A., M.S., Ph.D. | LPC, LPCC | Cannot prescribe medicine. Licensed Professional Counselors have specific training in the provision of therapy. |
| Marriage and Family Therapists | M.A., MSW | MFT, LMFT | These therapists have specific training in marriage/family treatment. Social workers sometimes have this additional credential. |
| Nurse | Masters in Nursing | Clinical Specialist —Psychiatric; Psychiatric Nurse Practitioner | Licensed to do psychotherapy. |
| Chemical dependency counselors | Varies by state | CAC, CCDC, LADC, many other variations of the above. May not be allowed to practice independently in some states. | These therapists have training in dealing with chemical dependency and codependency. Many therapists have this credential in addition to an LISW or LPC. |

links to state boards on his Web site. Go directly to http://psychcentral.com/resources/Licensing_Information/ for licensing information for your therapist.

# Additional Qualifications for Online Therapists

There are additional qualifications that are essential when doing therapy online. These are outlined below.

## Experience

Experience is a necessary and basic qualification for all therapists, either face-to-face or online. When working with someone face-to-face, the therapist has the benefit of what are called "non-verbals." Non-verbals are all the ways you communicate beyond the simple, spoken word. These include body movements, sighs, voice inflection, and tone. Therapists who think that therapy cannot be done online often cite the lack of non-verbals as one of the main obstacles to ethical and effective online treatment.

It has been my experience (and the experience of many of my colleagues) that despite the lack of non-verbals in text-based communication, therapeutic relationships can be established online. Experience is necessary, in part, because it helps the therapist be empathetic. A therapist who has worked with many others before you can use those experiences to help you and to better understand your particular situation. However, it must be stated that some therapists are just naturally empathetic. They can tune in to your situation and intuitively know what you are going through and what to say to you. An empathetic therapist will help you feel supported during the difficult process of therapy.

Generally speaking, I would recommend the therapist have at least five years of experience in face-to-face therapy prior to working online. The actual experience of working with people over time allows the therapist to access memories of what worked with clients in the past, which can help him or her guide you with your issues. Therapists need to be able to "fill in the gaps" that exist in chat rooms or e-mail; that is to say, they must be so familiar with the kinds of issues you are struggling with that they have a sense of what those issues are as you discuss them. An experienced therapist can almost finish your sentence as you type (of course, a good therapist would not do that). An inexperienced therapist doesn't have the memories of dealing with many different people over time to draw upon as he or she is trying to tune in to your specific situation, making it harder to understand you and see the world from your perspective.

## Appropriate Web Site with All Needed Information

Online therapists either have their own Web sites or are connected with an online therapy company's Web site. In either
case, you should be comfortable with what you see on the Web
site. If the therapist doesn't identify himself or his credentials,
beware. I wouldn't start a process of therapy with a therapist
who only identifies himself as "Dr. M." All it takes to create a
Web site is a little bit of knowledge about Web design and some
software. So, anyone can create a Web site making claims that
are just not true. Those are the people you want to avoid. All
ethical therapists' Web sites will include the following information:

1.  *Specific contact information, such as a telephone number,
    office address, and mailing address.* Contact information
    is especially important in online therapy. If your com-
    puter freezes, for example, you want to be able to con-
    tact your therapist in another way.

2.  *Credentials or licenses and links to verify those creden-
    tials or licenses.* Credentials and licenses are necessary
    to insure you are getting a therapist who meets criteria
    to practice therapy in your state and who is held ac-
    countable by the state board for the ethical provision of
    services.

3.  *Information about policies and procedures of the online
    therapy process.* Information about policies and proce-
    dures helps you understand what is a very new process
    for most of us. This information helps you understand
    what the rules are, so you can get the most out of the
    experience of online therapy.

4.  *Disclaimers and information about the limitations of online
    therapy.* The therapist should inform you that online
    therapy is but one way to get involved in the therapy
    process, that most people seek face-to-face therapy, and
    that online therapy doesn't have the research to back up
    its effectiveness that other types of therapy do. The dis-
    claimer should talk about the problems with online
    therapy—that the therapist can't see you and so will miss
    the non-verbal cues, that the therapist can't intervene

with you in the same way he could if you and he were in the same room, and so on.

5. *Specific information about fees.* You need information about fees before you can make a decision about choosing a therapist, even if you are wealthy. If a therapist isn't forthcoming about fees, or if you get a feeling from the Web site that the therapist is mostly interested in the money, these are areas of concern. Fees have to be a consideration, but really shouldn't be the main factor in your decision. You must keep in mind, however, that the money you spend on therapy with a good therapist is a wise investment for you and for your future. My advice: cut some corners on your grocery bill, but don't sacrifice quality for a few dollars when choosing a therapist.

## Typing/Spelling/Grammar

These are essential skills in online therapy. Since the type-written word is the medium—the only medium for chat and e-mail therapy—then it stands to reason that the competent online therapist should be very good at all of these things. I'm sure there are clinicians who are excellent in face-to-face therapy who will never be able to make the transition to online therapy because of difficulty in one of these areas. It's a good thing online therapy doesn't depend on handwriting, or most of us would be sunk!

The chat room therapist should be a good typist and be able to type at close to a conversational speed. This is less important for therapy by e-mail, where one can take time and correct any typos. In the chat room, the therapist needs to respond, some-times rather quickly, to what is being said in the session. The better the therapist is at typing, the more closely the session corresponds to a face-to-face session. Does the therapist have to be a touch typist? Absolutely not. I've worked with a psychia-trist who had to do charting electronically at the hospital where we worked, and he had no typing experience. In short order, using his two index fingers, he was typing faster than I do by touch. The main thing is that you feel responded to in a manner that fits the flow of the online communication. Be wary of a therapist who takes minutes to form a simple reply. Will the good therapist make typos during the session? Of course! (And so will you.) The therapist can correct the typo in the following response. One way to do this is to retype the mistyped word, and put in an equals sign followed by the correct word, e.g., corrct = correct.

Spelling and grammar are closely linked and are vitally important to online text-based therapy, because typewritten words are the mode of treatment. It can be distracting if the therapist can't spell or put words together in a sentence. Typewritten words are all you have to look at in the process, so naturally, they stand out. If the therapist can spell, type, and write, then treatment can proceed in a manner similar to face-to-face therapy. On the other hand, does every interaction in online therapy have to be grammatically correct? Absolutely not. As a matter of fact, sometimes abbreviated sentences and online "shorthand" make the communication flow more smoothly. The therapist will need to be both savvy and comfortable online to guide you in the process (if guidance is needed), or to participate in the usual modifications that happen in online chat.

## Online Savvy and Comfort

A modified sentence structure has been developed and is utilized by regular users of chat rooms. I don't know that these changes have been codified by anyone, but they exist. You have to have been in chat rooms to know what I'm talking about. Sometimes it would take too long to type a reply to a comment, so you type a partial sentence that addresses the issue directly. However, you then think of an addition to your reply, so you simply type the addition and the reader puts both together by looking at your two replies.

Abbreviations seem to me to be essential to online work. If the therapist is working from home, and a child in the home screams as he knocks over the coffee table, there is just not enough time to type in "Someone screamed in my home and I have to go investigate." What the therapist could type is "brb," which stands for "Be right back." While this should be kept to a bare minimum, it may happen on occasion, and you need to be aware if the therapist has stepped away for an emergency. (Incidentally, emergencies happen in face-to-face, as well, although hopefully at a minimum.)

The therapist should be aware of Internet resources that can help you deal with the issues you face. There are endless resources on the 'Net, and many could be of benefit to you. A competent therapist can help you sort out which resources are the best for you.

## Online Study/Supervision/Research

Good online therapists will be participating in self-directed study regarding the translation of their skill sets from face-to-face to online therapy. As online therapy is a very new field, its effectiveness is in the process of being evaluated. All ethical codes discuss competence of the therapist as one of the major parts of ethical behavior. The only way a therapist can become competent to provide online therapy is to participate in one of the several ways therapists become competent in the first place—training, supervision, case conferences, experience, and self-directed study. Not many therapists have been doing online therapy for long enough to be able to supervise other therapists, so much of the supervision is appropriately being conducted between peers at this point. There are groups of therapists who are getting together to discuss online cases in a confidential case consultation format, which is quite helpful and is a vehicle for both teaching and learning about online therapy.

The therapist you choose to work with should be able to discuss with you how he or she has become competent to provide services online. He or she should know how to translate face-to-face skills to the online world.

## Membership in ISMHO

The International Society of Mental Health Online (ISMHO) was formed in 1997 to promote the ethical provision of online mental health services. Currently, ISMHO has 125 members (made up of providers and consumers of mental health services). All members subscribe to the *Suggested Principles for the Online Provision of Mental Health Services* (reprinted in their entirety in Appendix B). Members have the ISMHO logo on their Web sites, signifying their agreement with the ethical principles promoted by ISMHO. More information about ISMHO can be obtained at http://www.ismho.org/.

## Checklist for Your Online Therapist

The following checklist is designed to help you see how the online therapist you have found measures up to the characteristics noted in this chapter. Your therapist may not have all of these qualities. If the answer is "no" to some of these questions, you have to ask yourself if that is acceptable to you. An example might be if you answer "no" to the question about typing; maybe your therapist makes many mistakes in responses to you, but you get such a good feeling about this therapist that you are willing to overlook this issue.

## Checklist for Online Therapist Characteristics

| | | |
|---|---|---|
| 1. The therapist seems to understand your issues, listens to you, and gives you the feeling that you are being understood. | Yes | No |
| 2. You get the sense that the therapist likes you and people in general. You get the sense that therapy is more than a "job" to this person. | Yes | No |
| 3. The therapist demonstrates a grasp of the bigger issues related to your problems and has ideas about how to help you. The therapist has dealt with and helped people with similar issues in the past. | Yes | No |
| 4. You get a sense from the therapist that if you talk about something disturbing, he or she will be able to handle it. | Yes | No |
| 5. The therapist avoids promises that don't appear sensible. The therapist explains what is happening in the session and what to expect in the future. | Yes | No |
| 6. The therapist appears comfortable online and provides guidance to you as needed with netiquette, resources, and so on. | Yes | No |
| 7. The therapist can type and spell well enough that typos are not a distraction to the online therapy. | Yes | No |
| 8. The therapist has a professional degree/training as a mental health professional. | Yes | No |
| 9. The therapist is properly credentialed, and this can be easily verified (if not already verified on the Web site). | Yes | No |
| 10. Information on how to contact the therapist is readily available. | Yes | No |
| 11. The therapist partcipates in online study/supervision or case consultation. | Yes | No |

Directions: Circle the appropriate response.

*Helphorizons.com home page (http://www.helphorizons.com.) provides mental health-related content, as well as information about the company's online therapy services. Reprinted with permission.*

# Chapter 4

## Nuts and Bolts—
## Practical Issues in Online Therapy

There are four mediums for therapy online: video, audio, e-mail, and chat. Therapy using video over the Internet is not widely used at this point because of the expense of the equipment involved and bandwidth (the amount of data transmitted over the Internet) needed. Services using video over the Internet are being used in medical health, corrections, and in other government applications and will someday be more readily available to private therapists. Audio is available to both therapists and potential clients and is used currently in counseling. However, the focus of this book is on text-based interactions between you and your therapist.

### E-Mail

E-mail is one of the most prevalent modalities of online therapy available today. E-mail is called asynchronous communication—communication between you and your therapist happens at different times. E-mail messages can be composed over a period of time and can be edited, so your thoughts are expressed exactly as you want them to be. A record of the e-mails can be kept and referred to at a later date.

E-mail can be used for a single exchange between you and the therapist—to ask information about a question that has been bothering you, or to seek some guidance for a decision you have to make. Sometimes all we need is a bit of information. E-mail can also be used for more in-depth issues and problems. You can have a long-term e-mail relationship with your therapist. People have developed productive, therapeutic relationships with their therapists using e-mail.

## E-Mail Security

E-mail can easily be encrypted using one of the software programs available. PGP (Pretty Good Privacy) is a software program that encrypts e-mail so that only the intended receiver can read it. You can obtain a free copy of PGP for non-commercial use at http://Web.mit.edu/network/pgp.html. You can also get information about setting up and using PGP at http://www.skuz.net/pgp4dummies. A commercial version of PGP can be obtained at http://www.pgp.com/products/dtop-security/default-encryption.asp.

Another e-mail encryption program used by some online therapists is Zixmail. It is quite easy to download and use. You can send and receive e-mail and attachments through this process (and also get a return receipt showing when it was delivered and read). The software can be downloaded from http://www.zixmail.com/. The charge for this service is $24 per year per user.

Some online therapy groups or clinics have developed their own software or procedures to keep your e-mail correspondence confidential. Etherapy.com (http://www.etherapy.com) actually uses secure forms on its Web site for communication between client and therapist. All correspondence between the client and therapist stays on the server computer at etherapy.com and so is protected from interception, because the e-mail doesn't travel from one computer to another as it does in regular e-mail. Etherapy.com states their encrypted e-mail is better than standard e-mail because it doesn't get sent through these regular e-mail channels.

## Chat

Chat is becoming more popular with therapists online. Chat is synchronous communication—the interaction between the therapist and client happens in real time. You say something and the therapist responds. Chat is my preferred modality of online therapy. It approximates a face-to-face therapy session in its timing and cadence. Although it is synchronous communication, chat enables you to edit your replies before you hit the send button. I've found that quite useful in being able to respond to an issue raised by a person in the session. I can think about exactly what I want to say by typing it out first and seeing how it looks. If it doesn't quite fit, I hit the delete button and start over again.

Chat can be used for brief interactions between you and your therapist. You can seek feedback about a decision you need to make, get information and a referral if needed, or have a brief interaction about a problem or issue. You can also use chat for long term, in-depth work with a therapist.

Some therapists don't believe that in-depth work can happen using the modality of chat. They say it's impossible to develop a therapeutic relationship with a person sight unseen. Most therapists who have actually provided online therapy report they are in fact able to establish quality therapeutic relationships online. In all likelihood, future research should validate these reports.

### A Sample Chat Session

Below is a hypothetical chat conversation between a client and a therapist. Endless varieties of interactions can occur in a chat room—as many varieties as there are therapists and clients. So, to pick a single chat interaction that might capture some of the possibilities of chat room therapy is quite difficult. We have to start somewhere, though. I've created an interaction between a therapist and a client that talks about feelings, boundaries, and changes made in therapy.

*Therapist:* You've been working on your feelings, as uncomfortable as that has been.

*Client:* but I haven't really changed them

*Therapist:* I don't know about that. Have you developed more of an acceptance

*Therapist:* of your feelings?

*Client:* hmmm

*Client:* yeah. I think I have...at least I've become more aware of them..

*Therapist:* and more open—at least with me.

*Client:* I'm not sure I totally accept them

*Therapist:* "more" of an acceptance.

*Client:* oh.. ok..

*Client:* LOL

*Client:* yeah..

*Therapist:* I don't think the goal is total acceptance—don't think it's realistic.

*Client:* oh good

*Client:* :o)

*Therapist:* I mean, who wants to feel bad?

*Client:* :o) good point

*Therapist:* Is it true you are understanding more about what you are responsible for

*Therapist:* and what others are responsible for?

*Therapist:* and you see the difference?

*Client:* <sigh> I think so... that's a tough one though

*Therapist:* yeah, when we really understand this, we can't escape our powerlessness.

*Therapist:* it's a tough one.

*Client:* yeah

*Therapist:* so what else are you learning or changing?

*Client:* well... for one thing... I think I'm not

*Client:* hmmm I'm looking for the right word...

*Client:* I feel like I can

*Client:* LOL

*Therapist:* you feel like you can laugh out loud? :0)

*Client:* LOL

*Client:* no....

*Client:* if I don't like something that is happening to me...

*Client:* instead of letting it happen.

*Client:* I think lately I try to do something about it, instead of letting it happen to me.

*Therapist:* you know, that's the best news I've heard all day!

*Client:* lol why?

*Therapist:* I think it's wonderful.

*Client:* I didn't say that I was always successful—I haven't gotten it down pat yet.

*Client:* :o)

*Therapist:* well, this way you have the possibility of success—

*Client:* :o)

*Therapist:* letting things happen to you—no chance. You're a doormat.

*Client:* yeah... you're right

*Therapist:* good.

*Therapist*: are there other things you are doing differently since being in therapy?

*Client:* ummm

*Client:* well... actually....

*Client:* if you told me that I would be talking to someone like this... I would have told you

*Client:* you were crazy

*Therapist*: hmmm

*Therapist*: that is quite a change.

*Client:* :o) I've never talked to anyone like this before. I've never been this open before.

*Therapist*: I'm happy for you that we are able to talk.

*Client:* :o) me too. It still kind of scares me though sometimes

*Therapist*: it's a scary thing.

*Therapist*: to be open and vulnerable.

*Client:* yeah

*Therapist*: also very powerful.

*Client:* why do you say that?

*Therapist*: it's the truth.

*Therapist*: it's what I see

*Therapist*: it takes strength and power to be honest and open.

*Client:* when you are open and vulnerable.. there is always that possibility of being hurt

*Therapist:* yes

*Therapist:* and the same possibility exists when you are closed and guarded.

*Client:* well not as much... especially if you have become numb...

*Therapist:* maybe.

*Therapist:* I just haven't seen people who are closed and guarded not be hurt.

*Therapist:* does it take strength for you to do some of the new things you are doing?

*Therapist:* talking as openly as you are? facing situations? and so on.

*Client:* I think so... it is not a natural thing... usually i have to make an effort

*Therapist:* that's part of the difference.

*Therapist:* it is easier to go along than to stand up.

*Client:* true

*Therapist:* but there is a consequence for the easy way.

*Client:* what?

*Therapist:* shame, guilt, stuff like that.

*Client:* oh yeah... I know those feelings.

*Therapist:* and there is also a consequence for standing up....more freedom... :0)

*Client:* that sounds really good... I want some more of that...

## Chat Security

I have used chat on America Online and ICQ for online therapy. In neither case have I ever had a problem as far as security is concerned. If you and your therapist are both on AOL, the therapist can simply create a private chat room using the Buddy List and send you an invitation. There is a text box on the chat room screen that tells you who is in the room. You and your therapist will be the only ones in the room, and you can communicate privately. I've never had a case in which someone came into the private room I've created without my invitation. There is a similar process in ICQ, where a private chat room is created and then you and your therapist both meet in that room.

The new online therapy companies (such as those listed in Appendix D) are offering secure chat at their Web sites. This further reduces the minimal security risk that is involved. You and/or your therapist can record what you say in a chat room, however. You and your therapist need to talk about that—if you are going to record what is written and if so, how the record will be stored. If the therapist stores information about you on a hard drive, it should be encrypted or password protected.

## Finding an Online Therapist

You've decided you could benefit from online therapy. You have a sense of what you are looking for in a therapist. Now it's time to start your search. Here are some ideas:

*Metanoia.* This site (http://www.metanoia.org) is one of the foremost sites concerning online therapy. Martha Ainsworth has been an online therapy advocate for a number of years. She has created a Web site where you can learn more about online therapy and find a list of online therapists with links to their individual Web sites. Therapists are divided into four categories: E-Therapy private practices, E-Therapy clinics, mental health advice, and specialists. This Web site also lists fees, and it rates the therapists based upon their credentials and other factors. This one-stop online therapy shopping place is a labor of love for Ainsworth, who receives no compensation for her work in developing and maintaining it.

*Internet Search.* When I put in the words "online" and "therapy" in AltaVista (http://www.altavista.com), I got over 2,000 matches. Not all of these were for online therapists, of course. When I put in the same words in Dogpile (http://www.dogpile.com), I got a large number of hits for a number of different search engines linked to Dogpile. This method of finding an online therapist will work well for you in the sense that you will find all the latest listings. Therapists are creating Web sites and coming online every day. This is the method I used to populate the database of online therapists in Appendix D.

*Appendix D.* This appendix is a partial listing of online therapists and online therapy companies. No endorsement is given by this author or the publisher for any of these individuals or companies—they are listed only as examples of what you might find. They are not ranked in any way and are simply listed alphabetically. To be included in this list, the therapist has to have at least a master's degree, be clearly identifiable, and possess credentials to provide psychotherapy services. Several of the online therapy companies listed in Appendix D are discussed below.

*Online Therapy Companies.* As online therapy has become more accepted by the community of mental health professionals, online therapy companies have been created. These companies have the financial resources, as well as the mental health and computer expertise needed, to build secure, easy to use, and attractive Web sites to meet the growing demand for online therapy. While a few online therapy companies have been created mainly for the potential profit they can generate, the ones listed below are well designed, well thought out, and have the express purpose of helping people. All of these companies have their therapists' licenses or credentials checked prior to listing them on the service. Here are some examples of online therapy companies:

*Etherapy.com.* This company was designed from the ground up to provide ethical online therapy services to people in need. Etherapy.com can deliver secure, confidential therapy services over the Web. All staff are required to complete a training program that teaches the therapist 1) how to deliver services online and 2) the many issues that must be addressed in online service delivery as opposed to face-to-face therapy. The therapists set their own fees on this site. Etherapy.com is developing a re-source pool of qualified therapists in all fifty states.

Etherapy.com also provides additional content, such as ar-ticles and news. To find more information about this online therapy company, go to http://www.etherapy.com. (The author of this book is a provider of services with this company.)

*Here2Listen. com.* This company provides online therapy in a secure environment. In addition to having licenses and cre-dentials checked, therapists must provide proof of experience and education, as well as references from peers. The therapists set their own rates, which vary. This company provides other content for the Web site visitor, including quizzes, message boards, articles, and news. To find out more about this com-pany, go to http://www.Here2Listen.com.

*HelpHorizons.com.* HelpHorizons.com is an attractive, secure site where a person can go and get advice, information, support, and counseling online. The Web site uses the latest technology to insure security for all people who visit the site. Formed in 1999, this company states it has to date "assembled the largest roster of independent online mental health professionals in the world." Dr. John Grohol, Internet guru and one of the founding members of the International Society of Mental Health Online (http://www.ismho.org/), is the Chief Operating Officer. The therapists set their own fees. Besides online therapy, this site also provides other content, such as message boards, chat rooms, and articles that visitors to the site can access. Check this com-pany out at http://www.HelpHorizons.com.

*Mentalhealthline.com.* Mentalhealthline.com is an online therapy company that is providing many different services to site visitors, including referral information, educational materi-als, online therapy, public therapist Q&A forums, self help chat rooms, and lectures. The site provides live broadcasts of chats on a number of topics. This site launched an interactive, self administered online behavioral modification program designed to help people stop smoking, boasting almost 500,000 hits in its first six weeks of operation. For more information, go to http:// www.mentalhealthline.com and check out the stop smoking site at http://www.smokinghealthline.com/.

*Newspaper or Magazine Articles.* More and more is being written about the provision of therapy online. There have been major articles in both the *LA Times* and the *NY Times* regarding online therapy, and we will likely see more in the future. Online therapy Web sites are often referred to in the articles, and from there you may find an online therapist.

*Professional Associations.* I initially thought this might be a good place to find a referral for an online therapist. It was not. While all of these organizations will be able to refer you to a face-to-face therapist locally, or provide information about how to find one, none that I have found will refer you directly to an online therapist. In any event, these organizations can help you learn more about licensing and credentialing of the therapist you want to work with. The national headquarters for these organizations are listed in the table below. You can call these numbers and ask for the local or state associations. Also, many of the Web sites have links to state chapters of the organizations.

| Professional Organization | Phone Number | Web Site |
|---|---|---|
| American Psychological Association | 202-336-5500 | http://www.apa.org/ |
| National Association of Social Workers | 202-408-8600 | http://www.socialworkers.org/ |
| American Psychiatric Association | 202-682-6850 | http://www.psych.org/ |
| American Association of Marriage and Family Therapists | 202-452-0109 | http://www.aamft.org/ |
| American Counseling Association | 703-823-9800 | http://www.counseling.org/ |

## Fees

Therapists charge fees based upon their experience, training, and other factors. Generally speaking, the more experience and training a therapist has, the higher the fee will be. Common knowledge about fees and pricing often doesn't apply to therapy. The general belief that less expensive is better clearly doesn't apply. When you are talking about your mental health, you are talking about a very precious thing. You want to pay enough money to be able to find someone who can help you.

On the other hand, it doesn't work the other way either—paying a very high fee for a therapist doesn't guarantee that the therapist will be able to help you, or that you and the therapist will be a good match. What seems to work the best is to weigh *all* the factors (therapist's qualifications, type of therapy offered, your comfort level with the therapist, fees, and others), so you can pay a reasonable fee *and* get a good therapist/therapy experience.

Sometimes people want to negotiate with therapists about the fee. This may be because many therapists have offered a sliding fee scale—payment of the fee was based upon the ability to pay. In my review of online counseling Web sites, I haven't seen a single site that advertises a sliding fee scale. Therapists are feeling the pressure of cost containment as a result of managed care.

Whatever fee arrangement you make, make sure to pay the fee. With online counseling, many Web sites are set up so you can't access services unless you pay either by credit card or purchase therapy "vouchers" ahead of time by either check or money order. The fee that you are paying represents your commitment to your own mental health.

| Type of Therapy | Low | Average | High |
|---|---|---|---|
| E-mail (per minute)* | $.80 | $1.00 | $2.50 |
| E-mail (per e-mail exchange) | $10 | $23 | $35 |
| Chat – ½ hour | $20 | $42 | $60 |
| Chat – 50 minutes – 1 hour | $40 | $74 | $110 |

E-mail and chat therapy rates vary from provider to provider. On the bottom of page 56, you will see some information about fees gathered from a review of several online therapy Web sites.

## Confidentiality

Obviously, confidentiality is an extremely important issue in all types of therapy. This is a particular concern in online therapy. The fear is that personal information you reveal in an online therapy session will be available to someone other than your therapist. Technically speaking, the confidential information you reveal to your therapist could be intercepted by a third party. Is that likely? No. You probably have the same chance of that happening as you would to have a person with a miniature microphone recording your face-to-face therapy session. What is far more likely is that you could misdirect an e-mail that is intended for your therapist, or your confidentiality could be breached by someone with access to your computer accessing your e-mails or chat logs.

Another confidentiality concern is the possibility of having someone other than you sign onto the Internet service as you. When a person uses your password, he or she has access to your online files and appears (to all others who are online) to be you.

There are ways of dealing with all these confidentiality issues. Here are some suggested steps:

1. *Never give anyone your password to your online service.* When another person signs on with your password, he "becomes" you in the online world. Your password is you and when you give it to others, you in fact allow them to be you. This could be quite confusing to an online therapist who may see you signed on to AOL, for instance. If you have a master screen name that other family members use, then create a therapy screen name that only you have the password to, and use that screen name when talking to your therapist.

2. *Get into the habit of always checking the e-mail address before clicking on the send button.* This habit will serve

you well. How excruciatingly embarrassing it is to send a private and personal message to several hundred people on a mailing list.

3.  *Limit access to your files* to only those people you want to know your business. Never send very personal e-mail messages from work—your employer has the right to read your e-mail. Never get involved with e-mail or chat therapy from work. Again, your employer has a right to read your e-mail and other correspondence.

4.  *Talk to your therapist about encryption software for your e-mail and about security of your chat sessions.* You will often see information about encryption on the therapist's Web site. That is a good sign.

5.  *Talk to your therapist about how your e-mails and/or chat logs will be saved.* You have a right to know this information.

The therapist is bound by laws of confidentiality not to reveal any identifying information about you, or specific information about your case, without your express written permission. There are a few universal exceptions to this, including: 1) if you are in a medical crisis (for example, you need to be taken to the hospital by ambulance), 2) if there is abuse of children or the elderly involved, or 3) you are a clear danger to yourself or to others. In all of these cases, the therapist will act in your best interest, or in the best interest of the person at risk. Trust is essential in therapy, and you can't trust a therapist who would reveal information about you without your permission. All ethical therapists I've known and worked with take confidentiality very seriously. Confidentiality on the therapist's end is the therapist's responsibility.

Confidentiality on your end is *your* responsibility, however. You need to be responsible for who accesses your computer, how you direct your e-mail, and so on. You can keep the information you reveal online confidential despite what some say.

# Chapter 5

## The First Session

Now that you've chosen your online therapist, you're ready to get started. The first session is very critical. It can set the tone for a long-term therapeutic relationship. There are several issues you must be aware of and prepare for prior to the first session.

### Scheduling

It is quite important to consider when to schedule a chat session with your therapist. In most cases, you will be meeting your online therapist from home. When you are in an online therapy session, it looks no different to family members or room-mates than when you are simply "surfing" or talking to friends online. That can be a problem.

If you are in the middle of a very important exchange with your therapist, and your son comes up to you and starts tugging on your sleeve to get him a glass of milk, it's quite distracting. If your spouse says, "Come here and help me out with this...." or the famous, "Why don't you get off that *!#? computer!" it makes the process of therapy quite difficult. When you are starting an online therapy session, you want as few distractions as possible. Consequently, sessions should be scheduled when you are least likely to experience disruptions. Also, when you do schedule, make sure to tell family members or roommates that you need some privacy during the time of your session. It is also in your best interest if your computer is in a room that has at least *some* privacy.

What do you do if you can't schedule at a time when you won't be distracted? What if you are a new parent and you will need to respond to your baby no matter what time it is? You can schedule at a time when the baby is usually asleep, and let the therapist know that you may be taken away from the session at any time. If you need to get away from the session quickly, simply type "brb," which means "be right back." Respond to the emergency (or whatever is going on) and then return to the chat when you can. A good therapist will understand and work with you on this.

## Information About Yourself/Releases

Many ethical therapists will not do online therapy because they are concerned that they will not know who the client really is. Therapy is a very serious business and there really is no room for someone who seeks therapy as a "prank." As strange as that sounds, it has been said to happen. If you are serious about establishing an ongoing relationship with a therapist, it is important to give specific information about yourself in the first session. Providing information about yourself goes against the traditional teaching about not giving out personal information to others on the Internet. This advice goes against the traditional teaching for two reasons: 1) if you've chosen your therapist appropriately, you know who he or she is and 2) through licensing or credentialing bodies in most states, the therapist is accountable to you for his or her behavior.

The information you will probably need to provide to the therapist will include: your name, e-mail address, street address, telephone number, proof of age, and possibly an emergency contact person. The therapist will probably ask for other information, particularly related to the issues you present, such as family composition or medical history. Proof of age can be obtained simply through the use of a credit card in your name and is required to verify that you are of the age of consent and can legally consent to treatment. An emergency contact person is a very good piece of information to provide to the therapist, but should not be required. You would have to give your consent for the therapist to contact this person, and the person would only be contacted if you failed to appear for an appointment without notifying the therapist in advance or if you were in immediate danger of some sort. If the therapist asks for an emergency contact person and you feel too uncomfortable to give out a name because of privacy issues, discuss that with the therapist. This becomes much less of an issue as long as you inform the therapist prior to your appointment if you need to cancel sessions (which can happen occasionally).

The information you provide is critical when you or your therapist are experiencing computer problems. Even the most sophisticated Internet users can have computers crash, get booted off the service, or occasionally have difficulty signing on. In these cases, having a phone number where you can be reached can significantly reduce anxiety for both you and the therapist.

Some online therapists will require you to fill out a form prior to your first session, in which you give this demographic information and also information about the problem statement (see next section). Other therapists will gather this information in the first chat session.

If you do not want to give out personal information to a therapist because you want only a brief e-mail exchange, then simply let the therapist know that. Sometimes simply getting a question answered by a therapist, or getting a different point of view on a situation or problem, can be quite helpful. This is called reality testing. We need other people with whom we can check ideas out.

I've helped clients with a brief e-mail exchange, for example, when I didn't know anything about the person except an e-mail address. When a person has asked me to make a referral, getting the city and state of residence is all the information I've needed to provide a list of agencies where the person's problems could be addressed. I would not work with a person in ongoing therapy without basic contact information, though.

## Problem Statement

At some time in the first session, you should be asked a question something like, "So, what brings you to therapy at this time?" or "What are the issues or problems you are seeking treatment for?" Another way the therapist might ask this same question is to say, "Tell me your problem in one sentence."

I would suggest you think about this problem statement before you actually meet with your online therapist. You will probably say, "I can't condense my problems into one sentence!" I know—it's difficult. And you don't have to do it perfectly. Think about it, and know that the clearer you are about what the issues and problems are, and more specifically, what the central problem is, the better your therapist will be able to help you. Alternatively, if you don't know what the problem is, then the first part of therapy will revolve around figuring out how therapy can help you.

### Goals of Treatment

What do you want out of the treatment process? What will it "look like" when treatment is finished? These are very important questions. The more specific you are in what you want out of treatment, the more direct the work of therapy will be. If you have a clear sense of where you want to go, it's much easier to find a way to get there. The therapist works with you to map out the best way to get you where you want to go. The map in therapy can be considered the objectives—the specific actions you and the therapist take to move you closer to your goals.

### Assessment

Your online therapist will spend much of the first (and maybe a second) session assessing you and the issues you bring into treatment. Again, the more clarity both you and your therapist have about these issues, the more direct and focused the work of therapy will be. The assessment process will continue throughout your stay in treatment. The results of the assessment will help the therapist choose strategies to help you work out the issues you need to work on.

### Treatment Planning

Based upon the therapist's assessment of you, your strengths, and the issues you bring to treatment, the process of treatment planning will begin. The idea behind treatment planning is quite simple—if you and your therapist can clearly identify what the issues are and develop a plan to deal with them, then you will make progress.

As a client, you should be involved in the treatment planning process. After all, it is you that will be doing the changing.

You need to buy into the treatment process and whatever objectives might be suggested to help you make the changes you need to make.

## When the First Chat Session Starts

Here are some suggestions for the very first session:

1. *Be on time.* Be a little early, as a matter of fact. It will just increase your anxiety (and the therapist's, as well) if you are late to the first session. I try to get online at least five minutes before the start of the session to make sure I can get online and to get situated before the session starts.

2. *Be nervous.* You are going to be at least a bit anxious, and please understand that it is okay. You don't know the therapist, and you are entering therapy because you have issues that are important for you to work on.

3. *Be honest.* Let the therapist know who you are. Understand that this is all about you, so if the therapist suggests you do something that you don't want to (or won't) do, you have to let the therapist know. Don't worry about pleasing the therapist in the moment—therapy can't work that way. (You have to realize, though, that you will have to step out of your comfort zone if therapy is going to work.)

4. *Don't completely trust the therapist.* You have to take a bit of a leap of faith to start the process, but understand that deep trust is something that develops over time. You have to trust enough to be able to talk about your problems, but it will take some time to see if this therapist is the one who can help you make the changes you need to make.

5. You are welcome to *ask for what you need* as far as scheduling times and frequency, therapist availability through e-mail, and so on. The therapist has to make decisions about these issues—availability, what fees to charge, how often to see you—these decisions are the therapist's, not yours. Good therapists will not always be available to

you, because they will have other things going on in their lives—other work, family, friends, hobbies, and interests.

6. *Trust your instincts.* If you have a good feeling about a therapist, and he or she meets the requirements outlined in Chapter 3, then go with that person. If you feel too uncomfortable to work with the therapist, then don't go forward, because it probably won't work well. You are not going to therapy to take care of the therapist, to focus on his needs/feelings, or anything of the sort. You are going to therapy for *you.* If a therapist's feelings are hurt because you decide not to return for a second session, that is for the therapist to deal with—not you.

## FIRST SESSION CHECKLIST

1.Scheduling: The times that are best for me—times that will have the fewest distractions are (write in best times):

Monday  Tuesday  Wednesday  Thursday   Friday  Saturday  Sunday

---

2.Demographic information (circle one)
I am willing to give out demographic information.  Yes   No
I am willing to reveal an emergency contact person if needed. Yes  No
Emergency contact name:          Phone number:

---

3.Problem Statement: I am seeking therapy at this time because (one sentence):

Additional information:

---

4.Goals of Treatment: When I finish therapy, my life will look like this:

---

5.List any concerns you may have about the first session that you want to remember to discuss with the therapist:

# Chapter 6

## Terminating Therapy

This book moves right from the first session (beginning therapy) to termination (ending therapy). The work—the process of therapy—is so unique to each therapy relationship that it is beyond the scope of this book to try and cover all the issues that might arise. To help you understand the work better, see http://www.aboutpsychotherapy.com/.

Once you've discovered that the issues you face are treatable online, and you've found a therapist who can help you, the bulk of what happens is "the work." Your problems are identified, your goals are taken into account, and a treatment plan is developed to get you from where you are to where you want to be. You terminate from treatment when you get to where you want to be. Sometimes, however, people terminate from treatment for other reasons.

### Unplanned Termination

An unplanned termination occurs when you want to leave therapy before you reach your treatment goals, or before the end of any contract you have with your therapist. There can be several reasons to leave treatment early:

1.  The therapy isn't working.

2.  Your financial situation changes and you can no longer afford therapy.

3.  A significant problem develops between you and the therapist.

4.  Other issues.

You might start out well with a therapist, but then somewhere along the line get angry or upset with her or him. It is quite important to talk to your therapist about what is bothering you. It is vital to make sure you have clarification about what the therapist is saying. This is particularly important in online therapy, because you and the therapist don't have the luxury of the non-verbals we all use to communicate. If you think the therapy isn't working, but through communicating with the therapist find out the problem was simply miscommunication, you can resolve the issue and keep on working. However, you may communicate effectively with your therapist, and somewhere along the line feel that you and the therapist are not a good match. If so, there is no shame in facing this and letting the therapist know that you believe the therapy is not working. It's much, much better to talk about this with your therapist than it is for you to either a) keep going on in therapy and get more and more resentful or b) abruptly end therapy. Every therapist I know would want to explore this issue with a client to see what is going on.

If you find that you and your therapist are not a good match, the best thing to do, as indicated above, is to talk to him or her about your feelings. This is not so the therapist can talk you into staying in treatment, because that can't work if your feelings remain the same. It is more to help you process what is going on, and to help you understand what is happening in your relationship with the therapist. You can also get closure with the therapist through this process. If your feelings change during your talk with the therapist, you can try a limited number of further sessions if you choose, to see if you can resolve the issue that bothered you enough to want to leave treatment.

You must realize that some people who seek treatment have unrealistically high expectations of therapists—expecting that the therapist should be able to meet all or most needs, be available at most or all times, and so on. If these are your expectations, you will have difficulty with most therapists. A good therapist will discuss what he or she can and cannot do as a part of the therapy process with you in the first session, to deal with these issues before they become problematic.

## Financial Situation

Your financial situation may change, and that could make it necessary for you to think about leaving therapy. The way the economy is today, it happens far too often. Unfortunately, therapists often cannot reduce your fee, because they have their own expenses to meet. The best thing to do in this situation is to be open and up front with the therapist, and let him or her know what your situation is. If arrangements can be made, that's great. If not, then ask for instructions regarding the process of starting up again when your situation gets better. Ask for assignments to work on in the interim, so you can keep working on your personal growth despite the break from therapy.

Other issues may cause you to have an unplanned termination from treatment. Again, the best thing to do is to be honest with the reasons you give your therapist and to keep the door open for your return when your situation changes.

## Ethical Issues—When There is a Problem

Sometimes a significant problem can develop between you and the therapist. Hopefully, this won't happen with your therapist, but it can and does happen. Here are some examples of significant problems:

1.  *Therapist seeks sexual involvement with you.* This means the therapist wants to have sex with you, or talks to you about having sex together, or tries to start a sexual relationship, even after termination of therapy. This is not about a therapist talking to you about your sexuality, if it is a part of your treatment plan or part of the issues you bring to treatment.

2.  *Therapist seeks romantic involvement with you.* This is the therapist wanting a dating relationship with you. This is not a therapist showing care and compassion.

3.  *Therapist seeks economic gain from you other than fees agreed upon (exploits you financially).* This is the therapist trying to use the relationship with you for inappropriate financial gain.

There is never any justification for any of the above to happen between a client and a therapist. All the ethical codes I've read list these issues specifically as violations (and others, as well). There is no diagnosis or set of issues or symptoms that would justify a therapist to do any of the above with a client. If the therapist does (even if the client consents), he or she is always in the wrong and you should do two things:

1.   Stop therapy immediately.

2.   Notify the professional association and/or credentialling body with which your therapist is associated. (See page 55 for a list of associations, their phone numbers, and Web sites.) You can also go to Dr. Grohol's Web site at http://psychcentral.com/resources/Licensing_Information/

The main thing is not to continue in an abusive and exploitive relationship with an unethical therapist. There are too many good therapists out there for you to be involved with a therapist who doesn't have your best interests at heart. Filing a complaint isn't the easiest thing to do, but it can be quite helpful to you and to potential future clients who will be protected by what you are doing.

## Planned Termination

Ah! This is the best! A planned termination means you have met many or most of the goals you set out to meet at the beginning of therapy. Congratulations! This time can be bittersweet as you prepare to move on with your changed life, and you leave the person with whom you've developed a strong therapeutic bond. It is supposed to be this way. When therapists do good work, they put themselves out of business with you. And that's a reward for both you and your therapist. All your hard work is paying off in a changed life for you.

Some people may have a planned termination because they have gone as far as they can with the current therapist. If that is the case, then part of the termination process will include a referral to the next therapist in the process. I know in my own experience, I've worked with women up to a certain point and have referred them on to a female therapist for continuing work regarding gender issues.

To appropriately terminate in a planned way, you need plenty of notice to process the feelings associated with your leaving, particularly if you have a very strong relationship with your therapist. Summarizing is often a part of the process—reviewing where you were and where you are now. You may feel some very uncomfortable feelings as a part of the process, as well, and these feelings should be talked about with your therapist. People sometimes regress as a part of the termination process—kind of like saying, "Wait, I need some more help!" This is a natural part of the process and can be worked through simply by being aware of it and by talking about it.

Termination does not mean you can never go back to your therapist for more therapy if you need it at some point in the future. Many people go to therapy to deal with a specific issue, then go back again at some point to deal with another separate issue.

My hope for you is a planned termination after a successful time in therapy with someone who has helped you get to the place you want to be.   :0)

*Mentalhealthline.com is an example of an online therapy company. Reprinted with permission. http://www.mentalhealthline.com.*

# Chapter 7

## Closing Thoughts

Therapists have long been concerned about barriers that keep people from obtaining treatment services. Barriers such as geography, disabilities, shame and guilt, fear, and the stigma sometimes associated with seeking therapy have stopped people from getting the help they need. The Internet is changing all of that. With the purchase of computer equipment and an Internet Service Provider, a person is linked to an online world full of resources that can address his or her needs.

You can be that person. You can confront your issues with a qualified, professional therapist online. The barriers that may have prevented you from seeking face-to-face therapy are often simply not issues at all in online therapy. It doesn't matter where you live, who you are, what your social or community status is, what disabilities you have, or what you look like—we are all equal through the written word. Geography, class, gender, or race are no longer barriers to treatment in online therapy. The shame, guilt, fear, or stigma that may have kept you from seeking the help you needed in the past does not have to be an issue online.

The Internet can be a great source of healing in our communities, our nations, and in the world. When we hear about the Internet on the news, it is often about such things as pornography, sexual predators, and other negative aspects of the online world. There is much that is good occurring everyday online. More and more people are seeing the power of the Internet in establishing warm and caring friendships that don't involve ever seeing the other person. It happens every day.

More and more therapists are seeing the usefulness of establishing an online presence to help either their existing clients or new clients. More and more mental health Web sites are being developed to provide timely and appropriate advice to people who are in need. Much good can and is coming from the Internet.

However, remember that online therapy is still in the experimental stage. There are many unknowns to this process and many professionals who say, simply, that therapy can't be done online.

Online therapy is not for everyone (clients or therapists). If you or your health/mental health provider have determined that you need more intense therapy than online services can provide, then proceeding with face-to-face therapy at a level of care that is appropriate to you is the best course of action.

If you have read this book and have come to the conclusion that online therapy *is* for you, then:

- Choose a therapist carefully.

- Check the therapist out.

- Trust your perceptions about whether or not you have found a good match.

- If it's not a good match, keep looking.

My hope for you is that you will find a therapist who can help you obtain the peace and happiness you deserve. I wish you well. :-)

# Appendix A

## Getting Online and Basic Communication Skills

In order to get "online," you will need three things: a) hardware, b) an Internet Service Provider (ISP) and the software needed to connect to it, and c) a connection to the Internet. You also need to make sure a telephone line is accessible to your computer's location in your home or office.

There are many options available. This appendix is designed to help the person who has not had much experience with computers to make informed choices that will prevent problems later on.

The starting point in the decision-making process is with hardware. Once online, you will need to practice what is called "Netiquette"—basic online politeness. Also included in this appendix is a list of symbols and abbreviations you can use to effectively communicate online.

## Hardware

When we discuss hardware, we are talking about the computer and all its physical parts—the Central Processing Unit (CPU), RAM, hard drive, CD ROM or DVD, monitor, mouse, keyboard, and speakers. Let's start with the CPU.

### CPU

The CPU is evaluated by its speed—how fast it can process instructions. The speed of the CPU has been measured in megahertz, or millions of cycles per second. Now, computers are being sold that have CPUs measured in gigahertz, or billions of cycles per second. My recommendation is to buy the fastest computer you can afford. The faster your computer works, the more time you have to enjoy it and the less time you have to wait. The opposite is also true—the slower your computer works, the more time you have to wait to do what you want to do. If you are buying a new computer, I would recommend at least 400 megahertz, if you can afford it. If you can afford a faster one, all the better. Some people buy a slower computer because it will be less expensive; others buy a faster one because it will be better able to handle newer and more complex software. I believe in the latter—trying to buy the most computer you can afford, to delay obsolescence.

You may also make some choices about the type of CPU you have in your computer. You can buy a computer with a Pentium 4 chip—the latest available as of this writing. Pentium III is still a more common chip. AMD also makes a very good CPU chip, and I've heard computer professionals swear by it. The Celeron chip is less expensive. Again, I would recommend that you buy the fastest chip you can afford, with the idea that you will be able to take advantage of the latest software and get more use out of the computer before you need to upgrade.

## RAM

RAM stands for Random Access Memory. The concept of RAM memory is often explained by the metaphor of the desktop. If you have a small amount of RAM, say 64 megabytes, it is like having a small desktop on which to work. On a small desktop, you can't look at too many documents at one time—there just isn't enough room. If you have more RAM, say 128 megabytes, you have a much bigger desktop. With the bigger desktop, you can open up more files and spread them around the desktop. Stated simply, the more RAM you have, the more programs you can have running at the same time. More and more people are saying that computer users need a minimum of 128 megabytes of RAM today. Make sure you get at least 64 megabytes.

### Hard Drive

The hard drive is the part of the computer where all the information from the computer programs is kept, as well as any documents, pictures, and files that you create or download from the Internet. The size of the hard drive is expressed in gigabytes (or gigs). You can get a hard drive now that can store 20 or more gigabytes of information, which is a staggering amount of storage.

My minimum recommendation for a hard drive in a new computer is about five gigs, and more if you can afford it. The hard drive space fills up quickly with song files, movies, complex software programs, and so on.

### CD/DVD/CD-RW

All computers for the home should have a CD ROM player for two reasons: first, just about all software now comes on CDs, and second, it's great to use your computer to play music while you work or play. Now that DVD is becoming more affordable, it makes sense if you can afford to buy a new computer with a DVD player. DVD players also play music CDs, but you can watch movies on your computer, as well. DVD players also can load software, so they replace the CD player on your computer.

The CD-RW is a special CD player that can also record CDs. That is pretty amazing—you can store personal or business records on CDs and keep them for years without worrying about losing the data (as long as you don't lose the CD :0). For the appropriate functioning of your computer, however, all you really need is a CD player, so you can install new software.

### Monitor

If you plan to spend any time at all on the computer, buy the largest monitor you can afford and space permits. It will reduce eyestrain, and in short order you will thank yourself for buying the larger one. The larger the screen is, the more "real estate" you will have, so you can open more programs and work with them simultaneously.

What about flat screen monitors? Well, they seem pretty cool, but they are very, very expensive. Unless you have the money, or your space is so cramped that you absolutely must have one, I would wait until they go down further in price. You could buy another computer for what you would pay for a decent flat screen monitor.

## Mouse/Keyboard

When you buy a computer, the mouse and keyboard come with it. You can buy special mice that are cordless, trackballs that have a ball that moves so you don't have to move a mouse (good for cramped desk space), and mice with wheels that can scroll text by moving the wheel. You can buy specialty keyboards that are split to better fit the natural placement of your hands (but may feel quite *unnatural,* at least at first, for people used to typing on a conventional keyboard). If you are interested in something like this, go to a large computer store and try out different mice and keyboards until you find what you like.

## Speakers

Many computers come with speakers. You can buy speakers that make your computer sound better than your stereo system. Many Web sites have music or spoken words as part of the site, so it's nice to have good speakers. You can buy subwoofers that will wake the neighbors (although you probably don't want to do that). Also, technology is advancing, and in the near future, you might use videoconferencing as a way of accessing therapy.

## Catalog, Internet, or Store Bought?

You can purchase your new computer through a catalog, from a Web site, or at a local store. Many people have been successful with a computer purchased by phone or the Internet from one of the major sellers like Dell or Gateway. It's quite a simple process. You call one of these companies, tell them what you are looking for and what you can spend, and they will design a system for you. The other way to purchase a computer is to go to a store where knowledgeable and available personnel can show you different models in various price ranges and answer your questions.

If you are a novice computer user, it is quite important that whatever computer you purchase comes with **Toll-Free 24-hour Tech Support.** Don't be penny-wise but pound-foolish. This kind of coverage is not like buying the extended warranty on a stereo CD player. Tech support for a computer can make all the difference in the world when it's 12 midnight on a Friday night and your computer stops working properly. With the tech support, you can make a call and there is a friendly voice on the phone who will guide you through fixing your computer (and really, much of the time it can be fixed). If you get tech support from a number that is not toll-free, you can spend a lot of money on long distance charges while you wait for the tech person to help you. You can buy a computer for less if you buy from a company that doesn't offer tech support, but if you do, you will be kicking yourself somewhere down the road (unless you are particularly blessed and never have a problem).

## Internet Service Provider (ISP)

There are two different kinds of ISPs—those with content, and those that are a direct connection to the Internet. America Online (AOL) is the biggest ISP in the world, and is a content provider, as well. AOL has over 28 million members (as of April 2001) and is growing every day. As an AOL member, chances are great you will be able to find friends or relatives there, as well. AOL has channels with content in just about any area of interest you may have, from gardening to fly-fishing to home-work help for the kids. Some people complain that AOL is too sanitized, because it screens content for appropriateness. Others find that screening to be a good thing.

Of course, you can go from the content areas on AOL out into the Internet. All you need is an Internet address (URL) that you type into the text box on the top of the AOL screen. Additionally, you can install another Web browser (software that helps you get around the Internet), such as Microsoft Explorer® or Netscape Navigator® on top of the AOL software, and use that browser to do your Internet surfing.

Chat room therapy on AOL is simple, easy, and safe. It is quite easy to create a private chat room where you and your therapist can meet. There are other content providers, but AOL is definitely the largest available. It will cost you about $21.95 per month for unlimited use, as of Spring 2001.

Microsoft Network (MSN), Compuserve, and others are ISPs that provide content, as well. Several of these ISPs have provided large rebates in computer stores in exchange for the customer agreeing to use the ISP for a predetermined length of time.

These rebates have helped a number of people buy their first computers and become linked to the Internet.

There are a number of direct Internet connection ISPs—too many to mention in this book. Some of these providers will connect you to the Internet for free. However, to get this free service, expect to be exposed to advertisements.

Any ISP you select will probably provide you with software to install on your computer at no charge. Actually, when you buy a new computer, you will find all the major national ISPs represented already on your computer—you just have to choose the one you want and personalize the software with your name and other information. (Choose carefully—I've heard people tend to stay with the provider they use first.) The larger ISPs have software that is quite easy to install. The software walks you through the installation process and automatically configures itself based upon the hardware you have. If your ISP does not provide a software "suite" for your Internet needs, you will need (at a minimum) a way to dial in to your Internet service (Dialup Networking within Microsoft Windows® allows you to do this), e-mail software (such as Eudora®), and a Web browser.

## Connection to the Internet

The two most common ways to connect from home are 1) through a telephone line and 2) through a cable. For both, you will need a modem.

If you are going to use a telephone line to connect to the Internet, consider getting a separate line for your computer. It will always be a local call (provided your ISP has a local number), and many phone companies give you a good rate for a second line. If you have just one line, your friends may get angry with you if you are online a lot of the time, because all they will get is a busy signal when they call you. (However, services that tell you when a call is coming through while you are online are becoming increasingly common.) If you do use a phone line, don't get anything slower than a 56K modem. Nowadays, anything less is too slow.

If you live in an area where you can get a cable modem, consider it. It can be somewhat expensive to set up and maintain, but what a treat to have that much speed on the Internet! The Web sites you see will appear on your computer almost instantly! And if you use a cable modem, you don't need a second phone line.

## Netiquette

The Internet has its own set of rules that participants are informally expected to follow. Here are the basic rules:

1.  When you go to a new area, look for a file or a link called FAQ. This means Frequently Asked Questions and is just what it says—a document that contains answers to questions new people frequently ask. By going directly to the FAQ, you won't annoy online veterans who have been asked the same questions over and over again.

2.  Using all capitals in posting or e-mails is interpreted to mean YOU ARE SHOUTING!!!! Avoid the use of all capitals in your conversations.

3.  It is perfectly permissible (and wise) to "lurk" when you first get on an electronic mailing list (a list where you submit your e-mail address and then you receive all e-mails sent to that list). Once you understand what the list is about, and how people talk to one another on the list, then feel free to jump in.

4.  When responding to e-mail or a post on a message board, always take some time to think about your response before you send it. Many people have posted messages in haste that they later regretted. You need to understand that posting to a list can be a matter of public record—so your post may come back to haunt you.

5.  Avoid character attacks on others (also known as "flaming"), even when you strongly disagree with them. It's not nice and it makes you look bad. Besides, if you are that upset, others are probably upset, too. Take comfort in the understanding that we are each responsible for our own behavior.

## Online Symbols and Abbreviations

Online interaction doesn't allow for non-verbal communication. Our gestures and facial expressions are lost in a text-based world. So, how do we add the nuances we need to communicate without seeing the other person or being seen?

Characters and abbreviations can powerfully express feelings and add to our communications online. Here are some examples of these characters (referred to as "emoticons" because they are icons that indicate emotions—tilt your head to the left to read some of them) and abbreviations:

| | |
|---|---|
| :o) or :) | Smile |
| LOL | Laugh Out Loud |
| <g> | Grin |
| ROFL | Rolling on the Floor Laughing |
| :o( or :( | Frown |
| OTOH | On The Other Hand |
| ;o) or ;) | Wink |
| SO | Significant Other |
| K | okay |
| CUL8TR | See you later. |
| :O | Shocked |
| TTYL | Talk To You Later |
| ? | What?/Explain/Why? |
| BTW | By The Way |
| BRB | Be Right Back |

# Checklist for Buying a New Computer

On the next page, you will find a simple list with reminders about the basic minimum requirements for a computer system as of this writing. You will need to make adjustments based upon what you can afford, but remember to purchase the toll-free technical support if it is not already included. If you are checking out a computer at a company that doesn't offer this service, I would suggest shopping around some more. Even if you have a tight budget for your computer, an investment in tech support will make a big difference.

Please understand that these recommendations are made by a user of computers, not a computer professional. Use these guidelines as points of conversation with computer sales people, both face-to-face and telephone or online. Don't take my word for these things—go and look around. Read some computer magazines and see what works best for you.

One last thing: when you buy a computer, arrange to have it delivered or picked up when you have a couple of days off. If you are like most people, you'll start to set it up, get pretty involved in the process, and realize it's 2 a.m. before you know it. Enjoy!

## Checklist for Buying a New Computer

|  | Recommended | What You Ordered |
|---|---|---|
| CPU<br>1. Pentium 4<br>2. Pentium III<br>3. AMD<br>4. Celeron | At least 400 megahertz | |
| RAM | At least 64 megabytes (128 preferred) | |
| Hard Drive | At least 5 to 10 gigabytes | |
| CD/DVD/CD-RW | Choose what you can afford | |
| Monitor | At least 17-inch | |
| Mouse/Keyboard/ Speakers | Choose what you can afford and enjoy | |
| Internet Service Provider | Shop around—try out different providers, including free ones—see what you like... | |

**Make sure you have **toll-free technical support** 24 hours per day!

After you order your computer, it is usually a simple process to set up and get online. Most computers today come with very direct and simple instructions for setup. If you do have problems, call that toll-free number you invested in, and they will help walk you through the process.

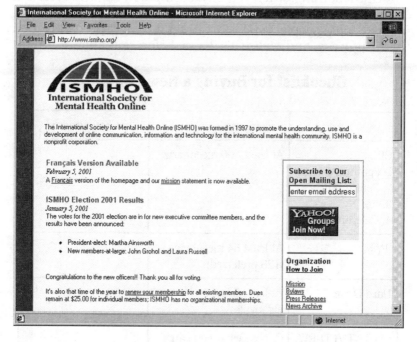

*The International Society of Mental Health Online serves as a resource on technology for the international mental health community. Home page (http://www.ismho.org) reprinted with permission.*

# Appendix B
## Online Therapy Ethics

With the increasing availability of online therapy and counseling, professional organizations are developing ethical guidelines in this area. Below are reprinted (with permission) the ethical standards pertaining to online therapy of the National Board for Certified Counselors, Inc. (NBCC) and the International Society for Mental Health Online & Psychiatric Society for Informatics (ISMHO/PSI). Besides providing guidelines and standards for therapists, these documents can help you, as a potential online therapy client, know what to look for when choosing a therapist. In addition to adhering to these specialized standards, therapists also have general ethical codes that apply to all members of their professions (such as the *Code of Ethics* of the National Association of Social Workers, which can be found at http://www.socialworkers.org/code.htm).

## Standards for the Ethical Practice of WebCounseling

*The relative newness of the use of the Internet for service and product delivery leaves authors of standards at a loss when beginning to create ethical practices on the Internet. This document, like all codes of conduct, will change as information and circumstances not yet foreseen evolve. However, each version of this code of ethics is the current best standard of conduct passed by the NBCC® Board of Directors. As with any code, and especially with a code such as this, created for an evolving field of work, NBCC® and CCE welcome comments and ideas for further discussion and inclusion.*

Further, the development of these WebCounseling standards has been guided by the following principles:

These standards are intended to address practices which are unique to WebCounseling and WebCounselors,

These standards are not to duplicate non-Internet-based standards adopted in other codes of ethics,

Recognizing that significant new technology emerges continuously, these standards should be reviewed frequently,

WebCounseling ethics cases should be reviewed in light of delivery systems existing at the moment rather than at the time the standards were adopted.

WebCounselors who are not National Certified Counselors may indicate at their WebSite their adherence to these standards, but may not publish these standards in their entirety without written permission of the National Board for Certified Counselors.

The **Practice of WebCounseling** shall be defined as "the practice of professional counseling and information delivery that occurs when client(s) and counselor are in separate or remote locations and utilize electronic means to communicate over the Internet".

In addition to following the NBCC® Code of Ethics pertaining to the practice of professional counseling, WebCounselors shall:

1. review pertinent legal and ethical codes for possible violations emanating from the practice of WebCounseling and supervision.
   *Liability insurance policies should also be reviewed to determine if the practice of WebCounseling is a covered activity. Local, state, provincial, and national statutes as well as the codes of professional membership organizations, professional certifying bodies and state or provincial licensing boards need to be reviewed. Also, as no definitive answers are known to questions pertaining to whether WebCounseling takes place in the WebCounselor's location or the WebClient's location, WebCounselors should consider carefully local customs regarding age of consent and child abuse reporting.*

2. inform WebClients of encryption methods being used to help insure the security of client/counselor/supervisor communications.
   *Encryption methods should be used whenever possible. If encryption is not made available to clients, clients must be informed of the potential hazards of unsecured communication*

*on the Internet. Hazards may include authorized or unauthorized monitoring of transmissions and/or records of WebCounseling sessions.*

3. inform clients if, how and how long session data are being preserved.
   *Session data may include WebCounselor/WebClient e-mail, test results, audio/video session recordings, session notes, and counselor/supervisor communications. The likelihood of electronic sessions being preserved is greater because of the ease and decreased costs involved in recording. Thus, its potential use in supervision, research and legal proceedings increases.*

4. in situations where it is difficult to verify the identity of WebCounselor or WebClient, take steps to address impostor concerns, such as by using code words, numbers, or graphics.

5. when parent/guardian consent is required to provide WebCounseling to minors, verify the identity of the consenting person.

6. follow appropriate procedures regarding the release of information for sharing WebClient information with other electronic sources.
   *Because of the relative ease with which e-mail messages can be forwarded to formal and casual referral sources, WebCounselors must work to insure the confidentiality of the WebCounseling relationship.*

7. carefully consider the extent of self disclosure presented to the WebClient and provide rationale for WebCounselor's level of disclosure.
   *WebCounselors may wish to ensure that, minimally, the WebClient has the same data available about his/her service provider as would be available if the counseling were to take place face-to-face (i.e., possibly ethnicity, gender, etc.). Compelling reasons for limiting disclosure should be presented. WebCounselors will remember to protect themselves from unscrupulous users of the Internet by limiting potentially harmful disclosure about self and family.*

8. provide links to Websites of all appropriate certification bodies and licensure boards to facilitate consumer protection.

9. contact NBCC®/CCE or the WebClient's state or provincial licensing board to obtain the name of at least one Counselor-On-Call within the WebClient's geographical region.

   *WebCounselors who have contacted an individual to determine his or her willingness to serve as a Counselor-On-Call (either in person, over the phone or via e-mail) should also ensure that the WebClient is provided with Local crisis intervention hotline numbers, 911 and similar numbers in the event that the Counselor-On-Call is unavailable.*

10. discuss with their WebClients procedures for contacting the WebCounselor when he or she is off-line.

    *This means explaining exactly how often e-mail messages are to be checked by the WebCounselor.*

11. mention at their Websites those presenting problems they believe to be inappropriate for WebCounseling.

    *While no conclusive research has been conducted to date, those topics might include: sexual abuse as a primary issue, violent relationships, eating disorders, and psychiatric disorders that involve distortions of reality.*

12. explain to clients the possibility of technology failure.
    *The WebCounselor*
    - *gives instructions to WebClients about calling if problems arise,*
    - *discusses the appropriateness of the client calling collect when the call might be originating from around the world,*
    - *mentions differences in time zones,*
    - *talks about dealing with response delays in sending and receiving e-mail messages*

13. explain to clients how to cope with potential misunderstandings arising from the lack of visual cues from WebCounselor or WebClient.

    *For example, suggesting the other person simply say, "Because I couldn't see your face or hear your tone of voice in your e-mail message, I'm not sure how to interpret that last message."*

*Reprinted with permission from http://www.nbcc.org/ethics/wcstandards.htm. Copyright © 2000 National Board for Certified Counselors,Inc. (NBCC) nbcc@nbcc.org.*

# ISMHO/PSI Suggested Principles for the Online Provision of Mental Health Services [version 3.11]

ISMHO has endorsed these principles, as per January 9, 2000. This is the only officially endorsed version.

Online mental health services often accompany traditional mental health services provided in person, but sometimes they are the only means of treatment. These suggestions are meant to address only those practice issues relating directly to the online provision of mental health services. Questions of therapeutic technique are beyond the scope of this work.

The terms "services," "client," and "counselor" are used for the sake of inclusiveness and simplicity. No disrespect for the traditions or the unique aspects of any therapeutic discipline is intended.

1.  Informed consent
    The client should be informed before he or she consents to receive online mental health services. In particular, the client should be informed about the process, the counselor, the potential risks and benefits of those services, safeguards against those risks, and alternatives to those services.

    a.  Process

    1.  Possible misunderstandings
        The client should be aware that misunderstandings are possible with text-based modalities such as e-mail (since nonverbal cues are relatively lacking) and even with videoconferencing (since bandwidth is always limited).

    2.  Turnaround time
        One issue specific to the provision of mental health services using asynchronous (not in "real time") communication is that of turnaround time. The client should be informed of how soon after sending an e-mail, for example, he or she may expect a response.

3. Privacy of the counselor
   Privacy is more of an issue online than in person. The counselor has a right to his or her privacy and may wish to restrict the use of any copies or recordings the client makes of their communications. See also the below on the confidentiality of the client.

b. Counselor

When the client and the counselor do not meet in person, the client may be less able to assess the counselor and to decide whether or not to enter into a treatment relationship with him or her.

1. Name
   The client should be informed of the name of the counselor. The use of pseudonyms is common online, but the client should know the name of his or her counselor.

2. Qualifications
   The client should be informed of the qualifications of the counselor. Examples of basic qualifications are degree, license, and certification. The counselor may also wish to provide supplemental information such as areas of special training or experience.

3. How to confirm the above
   So that the client can confirm the counselor's qualifications, the counselor should provide the telephone numbers or Web page URLs of the relevant institutions.

c. Potential benefits

The client should be informed of the potential benefits of receiving mental health services online. This includes both the circumstances in which the counselor considers online mental health services appropriate and the possible advantages of providing those services online. For example, the potential benefits of e-mail may include: (1) being able to send and receive messages at any time of day or night, (2) never having to leave messages with intermediaries, (3) avoiding not only intermediaries, but also voice mail and "telephone tag," (4) being able to take as long as one wants to compose, and having the opportunity to reflect upon, one's messages, (5) automatically having a record of communications to refer to later, and (6) feeling less inhibited than in person.

d.  Potential risks

The client should be informed of the potential risks of receiving mental health services online. For example, the potential risks of e-mail may include (1) messages not being received and (2) confidentiality being breached. E-mails could fail to be received if they are sent to the wrong address (which might also breach confidentiality) or if they just are not noticed by the counselor. Confidentiality could be breached in transit by hackers or Internet service providers or at either end by others with access to the e-mail account or the computer. Extra safeguards should be considered when the computer is shared by family members, students, library patrons, etc.

e.  Safeguards

The client should be informed of safeguards that are taken by the counselor and could be taken by himself or herself against the potential risks. For example, (1) a "return receipt" can be requested whenever an e-mail is sent and (2) a password can be required for access to the computer or, more secure, but also more difficult to set up, encryption can be used.

f.  Alternatives

The client should be informed of the alternatives to receiving mental health services online. For example, other options might include (1) receiving mental health services in person, (2) talking to a friend or family member, (3) exercising or meditating, or (4) not doing anything at all.

g.  Proxies

Some clients are not in a position to consent themselves to receive mental health services. In those cases, consent should be obtained from a parent, legal guardian, or other authorized party—and the identity of that party should be verified.

2.  Standard operating procedure

In general, the counselor should follow the same procedures when providing mental health services online as he or she would when providing them in person. In particular:

a.  Boundaries of competence

The counselor should remain within his or her boundaries of competence and not attempt to address a problem online if he or she would not attempt to address the same problem in person.

b.  Requirements to practice

The counselor should meet any necessary requirements (for example, be licensed) to provide mental health services where he or she is located. In fact, requirements where the client is located may also need to be met to make it legal to provide mental health services to that client. See also the above on qualifications.

c.  Structure of the online services

The counselor and the client should agree on the frequency and mode of communication, the method for determining the fee, the estimated cost to the client, the method of payment, etc.

d.  Evaluation

The counselor should adequately evaluate the client before providing any mental health services online. The client should understand that that evaluation could potentially be helped or hindered by communicating online.

e.  Confidentiality of the client

The confidentiality of the client should be protected. Information about the client should be released only with his or her permission. The client should be informed of any exceptions to this general rule.

f. Records

The counselor should maintain records of the online mental health services. If those records include copies or recordings of communications with the client, the client should be informed.

g. Established guidelines

The counselor should of course follow the laws and other established guidelines (such as those of professional organizations) that apply to him or her.

3. Emergencies

a. Procedures

The procedures to follow in an emergency should be discussed. These procedures should address the possibility that the counselor might not immediately receive an online communication and might involve a local backup.

b. Local backup

Another issue specific to online mental health services is that the counselor can be a great distance from the client. This may limit the counselor's ability to respond to an emergency. The counselor should therefore in these cases obtain the name and telephone number of a qualified local (mental) health care provider (who preferably already knows the client, such as his or her primary care physician).

*Reprinted with permission from http://www.ismho.org/suggestions.html. The ISMHO/PSI Suggested Principles for the Online Provision of Mental Health Services are Copyright © 2000 International Society for Mental Health Online & Psychiatric Society for Informatics. All rights reserved.*

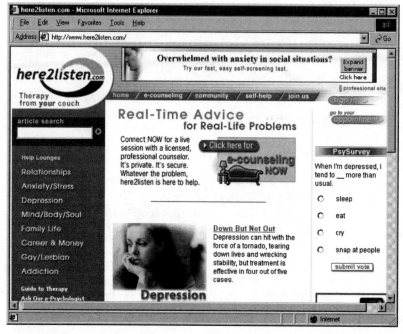

Here2listen (http://www.here2listen.com) offers "real-time advice for real-life problems." Reprinted with permission.

# Appendix C

## Types of Therapy

While it is beyond the scope of this book to explore different types of therapy in depth, this brief overview should give you some ideas and information in your search for a therapist. Many therapists today use an "eclectic" approach to therapy. Eclectic means the therapist may subscribe primarily to one type of therapy, but use approaches and techniques from other types to individualize treatment specifically to meet your needs. An example would be a therapist who comes from a psychodynamic background, but who uses Rational Emotive Behavioral Therapy and Narrative Therapy techniques in treatment with you, as well. There are literally hundreds of other types of therapy, but the ones included represent several of the major schools of therapy.

### Psychodynamic Psychotherapy

This type of therapy is one of the oldest types available. Originally developed by Sigmund Freud and then expanded by others, it looks at a person's childhood development and how it has affected the individual's current functioning. This type of therapy often uses the concepts of Id (generally referring to instinctual desires, such as sex and violence), Ego (the surface personality that one shows the outside world), and Superego (the conscience and the idealized view one has of him or herself) and looks at the interplay among these parts to determine how a person's current functioning is affected.

In the therapy process, the therapist uses other psychodynamic concepts to help the client develop insight into motivations for behavior. The therapist looks at the meaning of many behaviors and, over time, will interpret those behaviors to the client. Generally, psychodynamic psychotherapy is conducted over the long term, but newer types of this therapy have been devised for shorter-term therapy. For more about psychodynamic psychotherapy, go to http://easyWeb.easynet.co.uk/simplepsych/204.html.

## Cognitive Therapy

More research has been done about this type of therapy than about any other. The research clearly shows that cognitive therapy works for different types of issues and problems that bring many people to treatment (depression, cocaine abuse, some eating disorders, social phobia, and anxiety). The idea behind this type of therapy is that we can have negative or distorted thoughts that affect our feelings and our behavior in a negative way. The prescription, then, is clear: change the thought, and the feelings and behaviors will change. In cognitive therapy, the therapist likely will help you look at "automatic thoughts"—thoughts that just seem to come out of nowhere and cause some very uncomfortable feelings. The therapist will also help you identify "cognitive distortions"—thoughts that you believe are true, but which are not (e.g., the world is either black or white).

Cognitive therapy is usually shorter term than psychodynamic, and the therapist and the client must establish a strong bond over time. Homework is used, so you will need to be willing to invest time into the therapy process if it is to work. (That applies to all therapy, however.) For more information about cognitive therapy, go to http://mindstreet.com/cbt.html. Another therapy that is closely related to cognitive therapy is REBT.

## Rational Emotive Behavioral Therapy (REBT)

Albert Ellis developed this type of therapy in the 1950s. The basic premise behind this therapy is that A (the activating event) causes C (a highly charged emotional consequence) because of B (a belief system that is irrational). Ellis states that we all have irrational ideas and beliefs, and to reduce undesirable emotional consequences, we need to D (dispute our beliefs and thereby change them). This type of therapy involves the use of homework, as well. REBT states that if you change the belief, the feelings and behaviors will change (sounds similar to cognitive therapy). To find out more about REBT, go to http://www.rebt.org/.

## Humanistic Therapy

This therapy involves your working as an equal with your therapist. It focuses on your being responsible for yourself and on the fact that you have hopes and dreams that can be actualized through the choices you make. This type of therapy treats you as a whole person who has untapped potential. There are too many facets of this therapy to do it justice in a paragraph. See http://ahpWeb.org/aboutahp/whatis.html to learn more about it.

One of the first humanistic therapies that was developed was Carl Rogers' *Person Centered Therapy*. This is a non-directive type of therapy in which the therapist views the client with Unconditional Positive Regard. (Remember, we discussed this in Chapter 3.) Again, that means the therapist doesn't judge you by what you say or do; you are valued just for being there. One of the main principles of Person Centered Therapy is the use of empathy. I have discussed this, as well—I believe accurate empathy is one of the most important parts of the relationship between the therapist and the client (and research shows its importance, as well). To learn more about Person Centered Therapy, go to http://www.world.std.com/~mbr2/cct.html.

There are other approaches to therapy. Here are a few sources for more information:

http://aboutpsychotherapy.com

http://suite101.com/welcome.cfm/psychotherapy_self_help

http://mentalhealth.about.com/health/mentalhealth/library/weekly/aa021698.htm

# Appendix D

## Online Therapy Sites and Companies

The charts in this Appendix list 12 online therapy sites and 8 online therapy companies. "Online therapy sites" are defined as individuals or small groups of individuals who provide online therapy. These sites are run by therapists in private practice or small group practices. "Online therapy companies" are defined as nationwide (or global) operations that administer online therapy sites. They generally don't employ therapists—instead, they verify credentials of therapists and supply space, advertisement, and other services that can be used by the therapist for a fee. These companies also provide content (news, self tests, links, and games, for example) on their Web sites, much of which is very useful and (for the most part) free.

The listed sites are not ranked in any way, and no endorsement of any particular site, therapist, or company is made by either the author or the publisher. These sites were found by a simple Internet search using the AltaVista, Yahoo, and Dogpile search engines, and are listed as examples of the kinds of sites you might find in your own search. Included in this database are the Web site names and URLs, specialties, fees (e-mail per minute, e-mail per message, 30-minute chat, and 60-minute chat), and contact information. Sites that were a part of the search results that did not include identifying information about the therapist were not included in this database.

New online therapy resources are developing all the time. I encourage you to do your own search, using the criteria in this book, to find the one that meets your needs. An Online Therapy Site/Company Worksheet is provided on page 103 to help you organize your search.

## Online Therapy Sites

| Name | URL | Services and Credentials | Fees E-mail/min | E-mail/per | Chat-30 | Chat-60 |
|---|---|---|---|---|---|---|
| Anxiety and Depression Help Site | http://www.angelfire.com/co2/counseling/main.html | Services for anxiety and depression; M.Sc., Ph.D. | N/A | $AU40 (approx. $US21) | N/A | $AU50 (approx. $US 26) |
| Compassionate Counsel—Dr. Judith Schwambach | http://members.aol.com/_ht_a/drjudith77/pg000008.htm | Services for multiple issues; Ph.D. | $1.50 | varies, but you can set a limit | $45 | $90 |
| The Counseling Connection | http://www.counseling-connection.com/ | multiple issues; marriage and family therapist; marriage and family counselor | $1.00 | $15 to $30 average | $36 | $60 (50 minutes) |
| EAP Online | http://www.pil.net/~lgi/ | pre-crisis intervention; master's degree, state license, 10 years' experience | $25/15 min. | N/A | $60 | $110 |
| Net Counselors | http://www.netcounselors.com | multiple issues; Ph.D.; SWA | N/A | $25 | $30 | $60 |
| New York Online Therapy Services | http://nyonlinetherapy.com/index.htm | multiple issues; CSW | N/A | N/A | $55 | $100 |

The sites listed in this chart are not endorsed by the author or publisher. They are listed as examples only. Readers are urged to use the criteria in this book to individually evaluate each site he or she is considering using.

## Online Therapy Sites

| Name | URL | Services and Credentials | Fees E-mail/min | E-mail/ per | Chat-30 | Chat-60 |
|------|-----|--------------------------|-----------------|-------------|---------|---------|
| Psychoptions | http://www.psychoptions.com | multiple issues; Nurse psychotherapist | N/A | $50 (first session), $35 (ongoing) | N/A | $50 for 50-min. telephone |
| Psychotherapy Online | http://www.psychotherapy-online. com | multiple issues; Nurse psychotherapist | N/A | $150 per month | N/A | $65 |
| The Problem Solvers @ TherapyAve | http://members.tripod.com/ TherapyAve/ | multiple issues; Ph.D. | N/A | $20 for 1; $50 for 3 | see Net Counsel-ors | see Net Counsel-ors |
| Psychotherapy-Direct. com | http://www.psychotherapy-direct. com/ | multiple issues; licensed psychologist | N/A | $20 | $40 | $75 |
| The Therapy Office | http://www.therapyoffice.com | anxiety, abuse, many other issues; Ms.Ed., LPC | N/A | $30 (1st); $85/3; $25 after | $40 | $70 |
| Talk to Dr. K | http://www.apsystems.net/ online_therapy.htm | multiple issues; Ph.D. | N/A | $10 | N/A | N/A |

The sites listed in this chart are not endorsed by the author or publisher. They are listed as examples only. Readers are urged to use the criteria in this book to individually evaluate each site he or she is considering using.

## Online Therapy Companies

| Name | URL | Services and Credentials | Fees E-mail/ min | E-mail/ per | Chat--30 | Chat-60 |
|---|---|---|---|---|---|---|
| Etherapy.com | http://www.etherapy.com | Developing a staff of qualified therapists in all 50 states; dealing with multiple issues. | Fees vary by therapist. | | | |
| Mentalhealthline.com | http://mentalhealthline.com | Licensed or credentialed staff master's level or above; multiple issues including smoking cessation; broadcasts of topics of interest. | Fees vary; no charge for e-mail interchanges as of this writing. | | | |
| Find-a-Therapist.com | http://www.find-a-therapist.com | Licensed or credentialed staff (database of over 6,800 therapists), multiple issues. | Fees vary, no charge for assistance in finding a therapist to meet your specific needs. | | | |
| OnlineClinics.com | http://www.OnlineClinics.com | Licensed or credentialed staff, multiple issues, other content. | Fees vary by therapist. | | | |
| Here2Listen | http://www.here2Listen.com | Licensed or credentialed staff, multiple issues; other content. | Fees vary by therapist. | | | |
| MyCyberShrink.com | http://www.mycybershrink.com | Licensed or credentialed staff; targeting services for college students. | $55 for online session. | | | |
| Help Horizons | http://www.HelpHorizons.com | Licensed or credentialed staff, multiple issues; other content on the site. | Fees vary by therapist. | | | |
| The CyberAnalysis Clinic | http://www.cyberanalysis.com/ | "world's first clinic staffed by…doctors and nurses trained in the UK." | N/A | N/A | N/A | $65 (55-minute session) |

## Online Therapy Site/Company Worksheet

| Name | URL | Services and Credentials | Fees E-mail/min | E-mail/ per | Chat-30 | Chat-60 |
|---|---|---|---|---|---|---|
| | | | | | | |
| | | | | | | |
| | | | | | | |
| | | | | | | |
| | | | | | | |
| | | | | | | |
| | | | | | | |
| | | | | | | |

Use this worksheet to record the information you find in your search for an online therapist.

# Index

## About the Author

Gary S. Stofle, LISW, CCDCIIIE, is a social worker and chemical dependency counselor. He graduated with his Master of Social Work from Columbia University in 1987 and has worked with individuals, couples, families, and groups since 1984. He has specialized in the treatment of alcoholics/addicts and their family members, couples, people with dual diagnoses, DWI offenders, and people with general mental health issues. Gary has written articles on various topics and has completed a chapter on Chat Room Therapy for a  book to be published in the near future. He has worked online utilizing chat rooms and e-mail off and on since 1996. Gary is currently the Secretary of the International Society of Mental Health Online (ISMHO). He lives with his wife and two daughters in Westerville, OH.

# ORDER FORM

I would like to order another copy of **CHOOSING AN ONLINE THERAPIST** for a friend. Please ship to:

NAME _____

ADDRESS _____

CITY/STATE/ZIP _____

TELEPHONE _____

      Quantity ____ x $12.95 per book ................. _____
      Shipping/handling ........................................ _____
      Subtotal ....................................................... _____
      6% sales tax *(Pennsylvania residents only)* ...... _____
      TOTAL .......................................................... _____

**SHIPPING/HANDLING CHARGES:**
In U.S.: $4.00 first book, $1.00 each add'l book
In Canada: $6.00 per book
Outside U.S. and Canada: $12.00 per book

**PAYMENT:**
Check or money order enclosed for $_____. (U.S. funds only)

Charge my: ❑ Mastercard ❑ Visa ❑ American Express
Card # _____

Expiration Date _____

Name on Card _____

Billing Address (if different from above) _____

_____

Signature _____

**Mail this form with payment to:**
White Hat Communications • P.O. Box 5390 • Harrisburg, PA 17110-0390
Credit card orders: call 717-238-3787
or fax form to 717-238-2090
Online orders: http://www.socialworker.com

**CHOOSING AN ONLINE THERAPIST** *can also be ordered from any online or offline bookstore. This book is also available in an* **electronic edition,** *which can be ordered from* *http://www.socialworker.com/onlinetherapist.htm*

***THANK YOU!***

# ORDER FORM

I would like to order another copy of **CHOOSING AN ONLINE THERAPIST** for a friend. Please ship to:

NAME _____

ADDRESS _____

CITY/STATE/ZIP _____

TELEPHONE _____

    Quantity ____ x $12.95 per book ................. _____
    Shipping/handling ........................................ _____
    Subtotal......................................................... _____
    6% sales tax *(Pennsylvania residents only)* ...... _____
    TOTAL .......................................................... _____

**SHIPPING/HANDLING CHARGES:**
In U.S.: $4.00 first book, $1.00 each add'l book
In Canada: $6.00 per book
Outside U.S. and Canada: $12.00 per book

**PAYMENT:**
Check or money order enclosed for $_____. (U.S. funds only)

Charge my: ❏ Mastercard ❏ Visa ❏ American Express
Card # _____

Expiration Date _____

Name on Card _____

Billing Address (if different from above) _____

_____

Signature _____

### Mail this form with payment to:
White Hat Communications • P.O. Box 5390 • Harrisburg, PA 17110-0390
Credit card orders: call 717-238-3787
or fax form to 717-238-2090
Online orders: http://www.socialworker.com

**CHOOSING AN ONLINE THERAPIST** *can also be ordered from any online or offline bookstore. This book is also available in an* **electronic edition,** *which can be ordered from* http://www.socialworker.com/onlinetherapist.htm

### THANK YOU!